Grade 6

Treasures

Practice
Book
A

Macmillan
McGraw-Hill

A

The *McGraw-Hill* Companies

Mc **Macmillan**
Graw **McGraw-Hill**
Hill

Published by Macmillan/McGraw-Hill, of McGraw-Hill Education, a division of The McGraw-Hill Companies, Inc.,
Two Penn Plaza, New York, New York 10121.

Printed in the United States of America

2 3 4 5 6 7 8 9 10 079 09 08 07 06

Contents

Unit 1 • Take Action

Unit 2 • Saving the Day

© Macmillan/McGraw-Hill

Unit 3 • Great Ideas

v

Unit 4 • Achievements

© Macmillan/McGraw-Hill

Unit 5 • Turning Points

vii

Unit 6 • Yesterday, Today, and Tomorrow

Name _____

Each underlined vocabulary word is shown in context in the following sentences.

A. Circle the restatement of each underlined word.

1. Stan stood at the <u>intersection</u>, a place where two streets meet.

2. The huge wave <u>engulfed</u> the house on the beach, completely covering it.

3. The party ended <u>abruptly</u>—suddenly and unexpectedly.

4. Stan was <u>conscious</u>, or aware of, the sound of the ambulance.

5. He had a lot of <u>anxiety</u>, or fearful concern, about who had been hurt.

6. A falling and rushing <u>cascade</u> of water burst over the dam.

7. Stan saw the established way of doing things, or the correct <u>procedure</u>, in the emergency room.

8. Stan bought a <u>souvenir</u> at the little shop to serve as a reminder of his trip.

B. Choose two vocabulary words. Write a sentence of your own for each of these words.

9. _____

_____

10. _____

_____

Every story has certain elements. The **characters** are the people in the story. The **setting** is where and when the story takes place. The **plot** is the series of events that make up the story.

Read the following passage and fill in the chart.

"Look, I don't want to do anything today, all right?" Harini was sitting on the curb. "This is the only thing I'm going to do today," she said. Harini waited for her sister to reply but she heard nothing.

Maharet was standing next to her sister and had wanted to say something, but had not. She did not want to do much of anything either, but it annoyed her that her sister was making it difficult for them to get anything checked off on the long list their mother had left them.

"Okay then, we'll just sit," she said. She reached back and stretched her legs in the sun. She sighed again, and realized how nice it felt to sit and share a quiet moment with her sister.

Main Characters	Plot
1. _____	4. _____ _____
2. _____	5. _____ _____ _____
Setting	
3. _____	6. _____ _____

© Macmillan/McGraw-Hill

 At Home: Together, talk about the plot, setting, and characters in the passage on this page.

As you read *The Summer of the Swans*, fill in the Story Map.

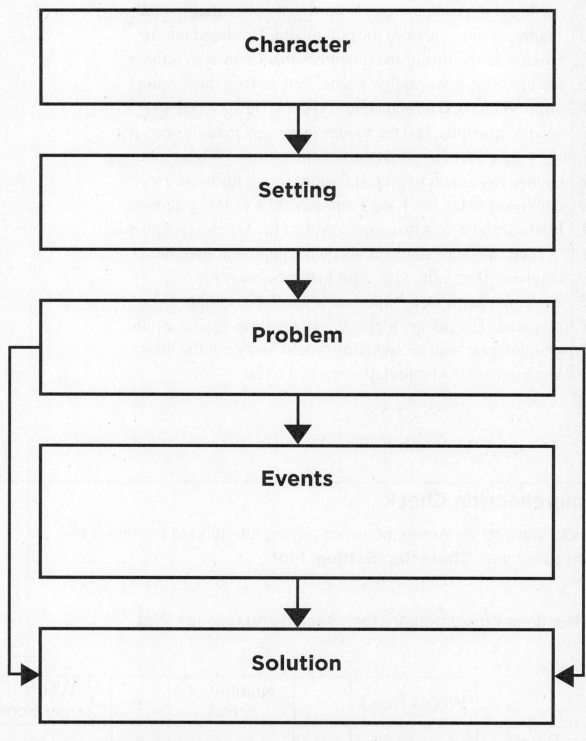

Character

Setting

Problem

Events

Solution

How does the information you wrote in this Story Map help you monitor comprehension of *The Summer of the Swans*?

 At Home: Have the student use the map to retell the story.

Name _____

As I read, I will pay attention to pauses and stops.

	Anderson tried extremely hard to be patient as his father,
10	Walter, double-checked the equipment. He stared out the
18	window at the tips of the pine trees that seemed to scratch
30	the blue sky. It was only October, but already the morning
41	air in Maine had turned crisp and cool. He shivered and
52	yawned **abruptly**, and the sudden movement made his ears pop.
62	Walter gave his son a stern warning look. When Anderson
72	opened his mouth to protest, Walter shook his head. He
82	continued to lay out King's equipment: a working harness,
91	leashes, and a vest that would protect the German shepherd.
101	Then Walter examined his own equipment: hard hat,
109	compass, flashlight with extra batteries, and radios.
116	Anderson knew how important it was for his father to be
127	prepared. The phone might ring at any time. Walter would
137	grab his gear, and he and King would hurry out the door.
149	Someone had to be found or rescued. 156

Comprehension Check

1. How can you tell Anderson is not paying attention to his father's preparations? **Character, Setting, Plot**

2. How does Walter prepare for a search and rescue? **Plot**

	Words Read	−	Number of Errors	=	Words Correct Score
First Read		−		=	
Second Read		−		=	

4 The Summer of the Swans
Grade 6/Unit I

At Home: Help the student read the passage, paying attention to the goal at the top of the page.

Name _____

A photo caption helps the viewer by explaining the context in which the photograph was taken. Captions give information about the people or events shown in the photo, and may answer the questions *who, what, when, where, why,* and *how.*

Look at the drawing of the photograph below and read the photo caption. Then answer the questions below.

Rooftop Rescue Wednesday, February 16, New Orleans, LA–Firefighter Randy Brooks climbs to where Lindsay Savoie and her dog, Polly, were trapped on the roof of their house by flood waters for more than an hour before volunteer firefighters were able to rescue them. Firefighters took Lindsay to a local shelter where her parents were waiting for her. Photo by Rebecca Broussard.

1. What is the title of the caption? _____

2. How does the title hint at the photo's content? _____

_____

3. Who is in the picture? _____

4. What is going on? _____

_____

 At Home: Together, talk about why photographs and captions can help people read an article.

Many words have more than one definition. These words are called **multiple-meaning words**. After you have looked up the word in a dictionary you can use context clues, or the information that surrounds the word, to help determine which meaning fits best.

Read each group of sentences. Then, after each sentence, write the letter of the correct meaning of the underlined word.

1. The carpenter hammered the <u>nail</u>. ____

   I like to buff and polish my <u>nails</u>. ____

   The detective used clues to <u>nail</u> the thief and arrest her. ____

   a. thin, hard material at the end of a finger or toe

   b. to catch or trap

   c. a small metal spike

2. The bride's <u>train</u> was made of lace. ____

   He took a <u>train</u> to California instead of a plane. ____

   My <u>train</u> of thought was interrupted by the doorbell's chime. ____

   a. part of a gown that trails behind

   b. a connected series

   c. a connected line of railroad cars

3. We took a long summer <u>trip</u> out west. ____

   A rock in the road caused me to <u>trip</u> and fall. ____

   The courtroom lawyer led the witness to <u>trip</u> up in his testimony. ____

   a. a journey

   b. to stumble

   c. to make a mistake

© Macmillan/McGraw-Hill

At Home: Help the student think of multiple meanings for the word *plant.* Then use the different meanings in sentences.

Name _____

> **Short vowels** are often spelled using just the vowel. For example, the short *a* sound is in the words *cat, bat,* and *rag.* The short *i* sound is in the words *dig, fig,* and *hit.* Sometimes, short vowel sounds have different, or **variant**, **spellings.** For example, the short *e* sound is spelled by the *ie* in *friend* and the *ea* in *head.*

A. Look at the word in the left column. Draw a circle around the word in the same row that has the same short vowel sound.

1. rug   over   though   done

2. bed   said   she   they

3. hat   came   may   glad

4. doll   shot   oak   colt

5. fish   myth   night   mind

B. Choose three of the words you circled. Write the letter or letters in each that stand for the short vowel sound. Then write a sentence using the word.

6. _____

    _____

7. _____

8. _____

 At Home: Together, think of as many words as you can with short vowel sounds, then list them on paper.

The Summer of the Swans 7
Grade 6/Unit 1

Read the following sentences. Use one of the vocabulary words to fill in the blank space.

undergrowth	venomous	escort	vegetation
interpreter	withstood	remote	foretold

1. The legend of the lost city _____ its destruction in an earthquake.

2. The carvings on the wall of the old building _____ centuries of rain and wind.

3. The lost city was in a _____ part of the rain forest.

4. Because he speaks five languages, Marco is often asked to be an

   _____.

5. The men cut through the dense _____ on the floor of the rain forest.

6. Everyone was warned that the bite of the snake was _____ and could kill.

7. Marco served as an _____ to the group of archaeologists in the rain forest.

8. The floor of the rain forest was thick with vines and other dense

   _____.

© Macmillan/McGraw-Hill

Every story has certain elements, or standard items. The
characters are the people that the story is mostly about. The
setting is where and when the story takes place. The **plot** is
the series of events that makes up the story.

Sam loved to hunt through the attic of his grandparents' house. Whenever
Sam went to stay overnight with Grandpa Hattie and Grandpa Joe, he would
ask, "Is it okay if Leo and I look around upstairs?" Grandma Hattie and
Grandpa Joe always said, "yes," and Sam would go running next door to
pick up his friend.

One day, the boys came upon an old trunk covered with a blanket. The
blanket smelled musty and the trunk was hard to open because of rust. Both
Sam and Leo had to strain all their muscles to lift the lid. Inside the trunk,
though, they found an old coat in perfect condition.

"Grandpa," Sam asked later, "whose coat is this?" Grandpa Joe smiled.
"Where did you boys find that lost treasure? My grandfather used to wear
that all the time when I was your age."

Use the chart to identify the elements in the passage.

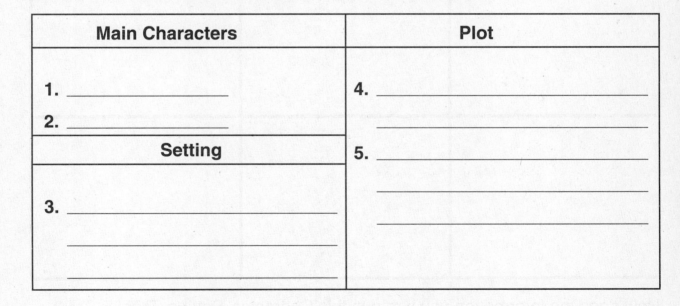

Main Characters	Plot
1. _____	4. _____
2. _____	_____
Setting	5. _____
3. _____	_____
_____	_____

© Macmillan/McGraw-Hill

At Home: Ask the student to draw a picture to illustrate the
passage.

Lost City • Grade 6/Unit I   9

As you read *Lost City*, fill in the Character, Setting, Plot Chart.

Character	Setting	Plot

How does the information you wrote in this Character, Setting, Plot
Chart help you analyze the story structure of *Lost City*?

 At Home: Have the student use the chart to retell the story.

As I read, I will pay attention to the pronunciation of city names, pauses, and intonation.

	Imagine finding a city frozen in time. That's exactly what
10	you'd find if you went to Pompeii. This ancient city was
21	once under the rule of the Roman Empire. It sits at the foot
34	of Mount Vesuvius, an active volcano in southern Italy. No
44	one has lived in Pompeii for nearly two thousand years. On a
56	bright summer afternoon in A.D. 79 the volcano erupted. It
66	caused one of history's worst natural disasters. Most of the
76	people living there fled the city as soon as they felt the first
89	shock wave and saw the sky darken. But a few thousand
100	people stayed behind. By the following day, the city of
110	Pompeii lay covered in tons of rock and ash. Death came
121	swiftly for those who had not escaped. The volcanic debris
131	killed them, but it also sealed their final moments. Today, we
142	can see how these people lived thanks to the volcano. 152

Comprehension Check

1. What was the cause of Pompeii's disaster? What was the effect? **Cause and Effect**

2. Why do you think no one has lived in Pompeii for nearly 2,000 years? **Make Inferences**

	Words Read	−	Number of Errors	=	Words Correct Score
First Read		−		=	
Second Read		−		=	

At Home: Help the student read the passage, paying attention to the goal at the top of the page.

Lost City • **Grade 6/Unit 1**

11

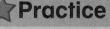
Social studies covers information about government, economics, geography, and history. A social studies **textbook** might include all this information and is almost always organized chronologically, or in time order.

Here are the main features that will help you use a social studies textbook.

Table of Contents—located at the beginning of the book; lists the book's units and chapters and their page numbers

Headings—located throughout the book; identifies the contents of the page or article

Glossary—located at the back of the book; defines specific terms used in the text

Index—located at the end of the book; includes an alphabetical list of subjects in the book with their page numbers

Answer the questions.

1. Where would you look for the beginning page number for Chapter 6?

_____

2. Where would you look if you wanted to find information on ancient Greece?

_____

3. Where would you look to find out what the word *pyramid* means?

_____

4. Where would you look to find out what the article on page 45 concerns?

_____

© Macmillan/McGraw-Hill

 At Home: Ask the student to identify the title page, table of contents, and index in his or her social studies textbook.

Name _____

> **Compound words** are made of two or more smaller words joined together. Compound words can be two separate words, as in *paper clip;* joined together, as in *paperweight;* or hyphenated, as in *daughter-in-law.* If you are not sure how to write a compound word you can look it up in a dictionary.

Study each part of the compound words below. First, write each compound word as two separate words. Then write a definition for each compound word based on its parts.

1. hairspray: _____

2. boyfriend: _____

3. toothbrush: _____

_____

4. zookeeper: _____

5. sidewalk: _____

_____

6. homework: _____

7. lighthouse: _____

_____

8. doghouse: _____

At Home: Together, make up a sentence using the compound word *backpack.*

Name _____

There are several ways to spell a long vowel sound. Study the examples in the box below.

Vowel-Consonant-Silent *e*	Examples: **bake, eve, hide, stone, cute**
Y that Spells Long *i*	Examples: **fly, spy, cry, try, why**
Vowel Pairs that Spell a Long Vowel Sound	Examples: **mean, beet, pail, coat**

A. Look at the word in the left column. Draw a circle around the word in the same row that has the same long vowel sound spelled another way.

1. paint   slap   pant   bake

2. bean   sleeve   bet   they

3. cry   crate   nail   light

4. cone   coat   tooth   pot

5. mule   cute   hug   noun

B. Choose three of the words you circled. Write the letters that spell the long vowel sound. Then write a sentence using the word.

6. _____

7. _____

8. _____

 At Home: Together, list as many words as you can that have the same long vowel sounds as *bake, eve, hide, stone,* and *cute.*

Name _____

> Each underlined vocabulary word is shown in context in the following sentences.
> - Scientific discoveries have <u>altered</u>, or changed, the way people live.
> - The force of water and wind causes rocks to <u>erode</u>, or slowly wear away.
> - A sponge is able to <u>absorb,</u> take in, or soak up water or other liquids.
> - When things are close together in one place, they are <u>concentrated</u>.
> - The scientist was known for her clever <u>innovations</u>, or her new ideas, methods, or devices.

A. Write the definition of each vocabulary word on the line provided.

1. altered _____

2. erode _____

3. absorb _____

4. concentrated _____

5. innovations _____

B. Choose one vocabulary word. Write a sentence using the word.

6. _____

_____

Name _____

Being able to identify the **main idea** of an article and the **details** that support it will help you better understand what you read.

Read the passage. As you read, think about the main idea of the passage and the details that support it. Then use the information to fill in the chart.

   Penguins are birds that do not fly, but their wings are adapted to swimming. A penguin wing is called a flipper. It is a hard, stiff paddle covered with tiny feathers. The shape of a penguin's flipper is like an airplane's wing. In the water, penguins gain speed by the up and down strokes of their flippers. Out of the water, penguins sometimes spread their flippers away from their bodies in order to allow heat to flow away from the core of their bodies. This allows them to cool down.

Use the chart to write a brief summary of the passage. Be sure to include the main idea and at least two of the supporting details.

_____

_____

_____

_____

_____

MAIN IDEA	SUPPORTING DETAILS

Gecko Glue, Cockroach Scouts, and
Spider Silk Bridges • **Grade 6/Unit 1**

At Home: Discuss the purpose of another animal's wings or
flippers.

Name _____

As you read *Gecko Glue, Cockroach Scouts, and Spider Silk Bridges*, fill in the Main Idea Web.

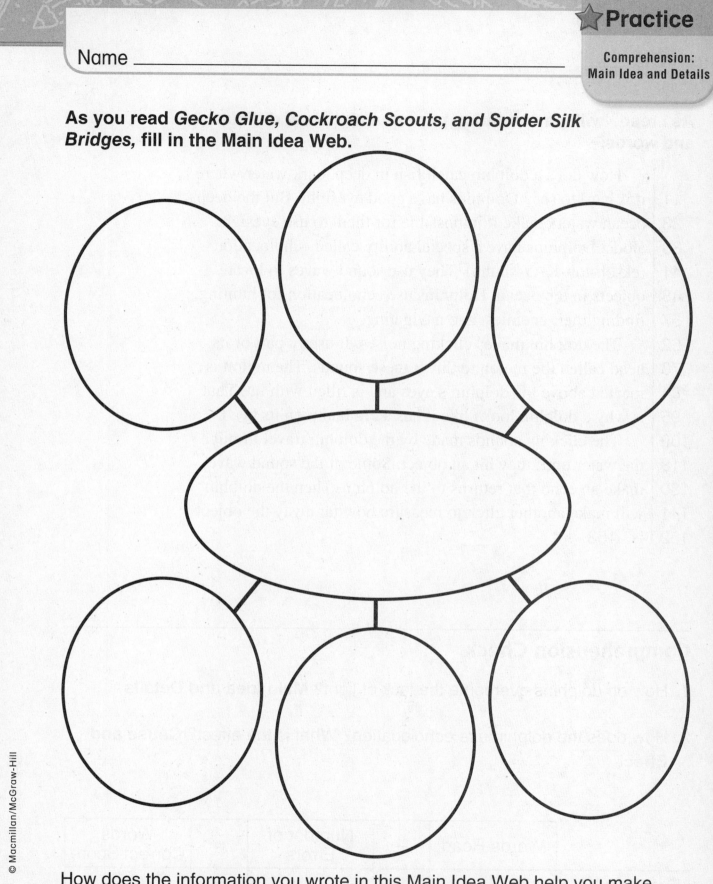

How does the information you wrote in this Main Idea Web help you make inferences and analyze the story structure of *Gecko Glue, Cockroach Scouts, and Spider Silk Bridges*?

 At Home: Have the student use the chart to retell the story.

Name _____

As I read, I will pay attention to pronunciation of difficult and words.

	How does a dolphin catch fish in deep, dark water where
11	it is hard to see? Dolphins have good eyesight. But the deep
23	ocean waters make it impossible for them to use eyesight
33	alone. Dolphins have a special ability called echolocation
41	(ek-oh-loh-KAY-shuhn). They use sound waves to locate
48	objects in the ocean. Dolphins use echolocation for hunting,
57	finding their enemies, and navigating.
62	The dolphin makes clicking noises. It uses a part of its
73	head called the melon to direct these sounds. The melon is
84	located above the dolphin's eyes and is filled with fat. That
95	is why a dolphin looks like it has a big bump on its head.
109	The clicking sounds made by the dolphin travel through
118	the water until they hit an object. Some of the sound waves
130	make an echo that returns to the dolphin. Then the dolphin
141	will make another click to measure how far away the object
152	is. 153

Comprehension Check

1. How do dolphins overcome the lack of light? **Main Idea and Details**

2. How does the dolphin use echolocation? What is the effect? **Cause and Effect**

	Words Read	–	Number of Errors	=	Words Correct Score
First Read		–		=	
Second Read		–		=	

Gecko Glue, Cockroach Scouts, and
Spider Silk Bridges • **Grade 6/Unit 1**

At Home: Help the student read the passage, paying attention to the goal at the top of the page.

Name _____

When you need to research a topic, you can use the library **media center** to explore the **Internet.** The Internet can help you find online resources, or information, through the computer. You can use a **search engine** to search the Internet and point you to collections of information, called **Web sites.** You can go to a Web site to find information, just as you can look through a book to find the information. For example, if you want to find out about spiders, you can use a search engine and type in the **key word** *spiders.* This will bring up a list of Web sites that contain information about spiders.

Usually a Web site will contain underlined words called **links** you can click on. Clicking on these links will take you to another site with related information.

One student found this Web site by using a search engine and typing in the word: *spiders.*
http://www.everythingabout.net/articles/biology/animals/arthropods/ arachnids/spiders/

Use the information above to answer the questions.

1. What is the address of the Web site? _____
   _____

2. How is the Internet like a library in a computer? _____
   _____
   _____

3. Which tool will help you search the Internet for information?
   _____

4. What key word did the student use to research her topic? _____

At Home: Together, make a list of key words you could use to find information about other animals

Gecko Glue, Cockroach Scouts, and Spider Silk Bridges • **Grade 6/Unit 1**

19

Name _____

A. Use definitions to help you figure out the meaning of the underlined words below. Write the definition that helped you determine each meaning in the chart.

1. Kaitlyn has decided to study <u>astronomy</u> in college because she has always been interested in the science of the stars and the planets.

2. Kaitlyn knows that everything she learns will be <u>beneficial</u>, or helpful, to her future career.

3. She is now studying the <u>constellation</u> Orion, a group of stars that looks like a hunter.

4. Kaitlyn's telescope has a <u>concave</u> lens, a lens that curves inward, so that she can see farther into the night skies.

WORD	DEFINITION
astronomy	
beneficial	
constellation	
concave	

B. Now choose one word and use it in a sentence of your own.

5. _____

_____

© Macmillan/McGraw-Hill

At Home: Find the context clue in the sentence: *Kaitlyn wants to become an adult, a person who is grown up.*

Sometimes two vowels together stand for a long vowel sound.
- The long *e* sound can be spelled by **ei** or **ie**. Long *e* is spelled *ei* in the word *receive*. Long *e* is spelled *ie* in the word *believe*.
- The long *a* sound can be spelled *ei*. Long *a* is spelled *ei* in the word *weigh*.

To remember how to spell words with *ei* and *ie,* memorize the following sentence: Place the *i* before *e* except after *c* or when sounding like *a* as in *neighbor* and *weigh.*

Read the sentences. Draw a circle around the words that have the vowels *ei* or *ie* together. On the line after the sentence, write whether the two vowels together stand for the long *e* or the long *a* sound.

1. Emma will be eight years old on Saturday. _____

2. Farmers are hoping to have a big yield of tomatoes this summer.

   _____

3. Did you receive an invitation to the party? _____

4. Kanisha and Mateo are my next-door neighbors. _____

5. Did you weigh the tomatoes on the scale in the store? _____

6. Raquel believes that her necklace will turn up again. _____

7. The salesperson handed Tanisha her receipt for the purchase.

   _____

8. Prakash filled the engine with diesel fuel. _____

At Home: Together, make a list of words that have the *ei* or *ie* spelling and identify the sounds for.

Gecko Glue, Cockroach Scouts, and
Spider Silk Bridges • **Grade 6/Unit 1**

 21

Name _____

Read the vocabulary words and their definitions.

chameleon: a lizard that can change the color of its skin

rummaged: made a search

scrounging: hunting around, begging, borrowing, or stealing

pathetic: causing feelings of sorrow or pity

undetected: not discovered

generosity: the quality of gladly sharing whatever you have

ricocheting: bouncing back from a surface

Find the vocabulary word in the rows of letters below and draw a circle around it.

1. thankyouforyourgenerosityingivingmeanapple

2. youwillnotfinditbyscrounginghere

3. whatastrangelookinglizardthatchameleonis

4. thewetandhungrypuppylookedpathetictome

5. sherummagedaroundinthegarageforanhour

6. hethrewtheballsothatitwasalwaysricochetingback

7. thediamondringlayundetectedinthegrassallday

When you read, look for **cause-and-effect** relationships. A cause is the reason something happens. An effect is a result of the cause. Look at the following sentences:
Madison stayed outside after dark to catch fireflies. As a result, she did not finish her homework.
Authors use words and phrases such as *so, therefore, because, as a result, due to,* and *then* to show these cause-and-effect relationships.

Read the following sets of sentences. Then fill in the cause-and-effect chart after each set. Sometimes the cause is mentioned first, and sometimes the effect is mentioned first.

1. Because Madison's family loved to go on picnics, they always planned a big one for the Fourth of July.

CAUSE	EFFECT

2. It was a family tradition to have potato salad at a picnic, so Mom made her special kind.

CAUSE	EFFECT

© Macmillan/McGraw-Hill

At Home: Talk about cause-and-effect situations that occur in your household.

The Magic Gourd • **Grade 6/Unit 1**

As you read *The Magic Gourd*, fill in the Cause and Effect Chart.

Cause	→	Effect
	→	
	→	
	→	
	→	
	→	

How does the information you wrote in this Cause and Effect Chart help
you make inferences and analyze the story structure of *The Magic Gourd*?

At Home: Have the student use the chart to retell the story.

As I read, I will pay attention to punctuation.

	How can you take a piece of paper and turn it into a cup,
14	a boat, or a bird? You can do it with origami
25	(awr-i-GAH-MEE). You don't need any special tools. All
32	you need is a design, your hands, and paper. The instructions
43	aren't hard. And there's no limit to the number of things you
55	can make. Once you get a little practice, you can even create
67	your own designs!
70	The word *origami* is Japanese. It comes from the words
80	for "to fold" and "paper." The word *origami* was coined in
91	the 1880s. It described playful folded forms. The art of
101	origami is much older, though. It goes back over 1,000
111	years.
112	This book will tell you more about the history of origami.
123	You'll also learn about new ways to create origami designs.
133	And you'll read about the greatest paper folder of modern
143	times. To top it off, you'll get to fold your own origami
155	crane, which is a very special bird. 162

Comprehension Check

1. How does origami's simplicity make it popular? **Cause and Effect**

2. Why is origami considered art? **Draw Conclusions**

	Words Read	−	Number of Errors	=	Words Correct Score
First Read		−		=	
Second Read		−		=	

At Home: Help the student read the passage, paying attention to the goal at the top of the page

The Magic Gourd • **Grade 6/Unit I**

25

Name _____

A **time line** can help you organize the many events and dates that you find in a story or other type of writing. A time line organizes information in time order. The time moves from the earliest event on the left to the latest event on the right.

Time lines are often used to show events that happened over decades or centuries. The time line below shows a period of time much shorter than a typical time line. Use it to answer the questions below.

Connor's Morning

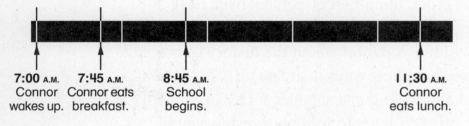

7:00 A.M.   7:45 A.M.   8:45 A.M.   11:30 A.M.
Connor   Connor eats   School   Connor
wakes up.   breakfast.   begins.   eats lunch.

1. What is the earliest entry on the time line?

_____

2. How long after Connor wakes up does he eat breakfast?

_____

3. What time does Connor eat lunch? _____

4. What time does school begin? _____

5. What is the latest entry on the time line?

_____

 At Home: Help the student make a time line by the hour for his or her typical school day.

> You can often find the meaning of a word by using clues in the words surrounding it. One kind of context clue is **restatement**, in which the meaning of the unknown word is restated after the word appears. Find the context clue that is a restatement in these sentences:
>
> Some animals are nocturnal. They are active only at night.
>
> The restatement context clue tells you that *nocturnal* means "active only at night."

Use restatement context clues to help you find the meaning of the underlined words. Then write a definition of the word on the line.

1. At every family reunion, Pop sings the <u>ballad</u> "Red River Valley." Everyone loves this slow, sentimental song.

   _____

2. Pop usually sings <u>solo</u>. Sometimes, though, Mimi sings with him when he doesn't want to sing alone. _____

3. Pop thinks that music helps to <u>unify</u> our family. We always feel more like a complete whole after we sing together. _____

   _____

4. Mimi and Pop try to <u>promote</u> family singing wherever they go. They feel that help in the growth of family singing so family traditions will stay alive.

   _____

 At Home: Take turns making up context clues for words of your choice.

The Magic Gourd • Grade 6/Unit I   27

Name _____

An *r-controlled vowel* makes the *r* sound at the end of the vowel. Sometimes the *r* sound makes it hard to tell which vowel is being used in the word. For example, what vowel sound do you hear in the word *bird*? Is it an *e*? An *i*? It is hard to tell! Because it is hard to tell, *r*-controlled vowels are grouped together. Examples of words with *r*-controlled vowel sounds are *word, bird, corn,* and *turf.*

A. Look at the words in the box. Each word has an *r*-controlled vowel. Then read the clues below. A word in the box is the answer to each clue. Write the word on the line provided.

thorns	ear	surf	birds	hair

1. You can brush it, cut it, or curl it. _____

2. This is a part of your body you use to hear. _____

3. This occurs when waves in the ocean hit the beach. _____

4. These are animals that have feathers and fly. _____

5. Roses have these on their branches. _____

B. Choose one of the words above and write a sentence that uses it.

6. _____

_____

At Home: Take turns creating sentences using the words *hair, ear, surf, birds,* and *thorns.*

© Macmillan/McGraw-Hill

Name _____

A. Each underlined vocabulary word is shown in context in the following sentences.

Emma knew it was <u>vital</u>, or of greatest importance, to help protect wildlife. Most of her friends wanted to help <u>conserve</u>, or save, big animals such as the bear or wolf. But Emma had done some <u>analyzing</u>, or examining carefully in detail, the parts of an issue to determine their relationship. She <u>speculated</u>, or thought seriously, about the fact that smaller animals need help, too.

Emma was <u>propelled</u>—moved or driven forward—to help conserve the butterfly. She knew insects needed water to keep from losing too much water or moisture and becoming <u>dehydrated</u>. Emma planned a butterfly garden with an <u>embedded</u> pool, planted firmly in the center of the garden. Unlike bears or tigers, butterflies do not need to be made calm or <u>sedated</u> to be helped.

B. Write the definition of each vocabulary word on the line provided.

1. vital _____

2. conserve _____

3. analyzing _____

4. speculated _____

5. propelled _____

6. dehydrated _____

7. embedded _____

8. sedated _____

Being able to identify the **main idea** of an article and the **details** that support it will help you better understand what you read.

As you read the following passage, think about the main idea and the supporting details. Then use the information to fill in the chart.

Cobras are one of the most celebrated and feared snakes on the planet. Cobras are easy to recognize, in part because of their unique hoods, which flare when they are ready to strike or when they feel threatened. Images of cobras are often seen in art or photos. Cobras also appeared in ancient Indian and Egyptian art.

Cobras are also well known for being deadly. Some species of cobra spit at predators. These cobras aim for the eyes, where the venom will do the most damage. Ancient Egyptian and Indian religions respected this deadly weapon and held the cobra in high esteem.

Indian snake charmers also helped to make cobras famous. Cobras raise themselves upright instinctively and mirror the snake charmers' movements with their bodies. To a crowd, the snakes appear to sway in time to the flute music.

SUBJECT	MAIN IDEA	SUPPORTING DETAILS
		1.
		2.
		3.

© Macmillan/McGraw-Hill

 At Home: Discuss the main idea and details of another passage with the student.

As you read *Interrupted Journey*, fill in the Main Idea Web.

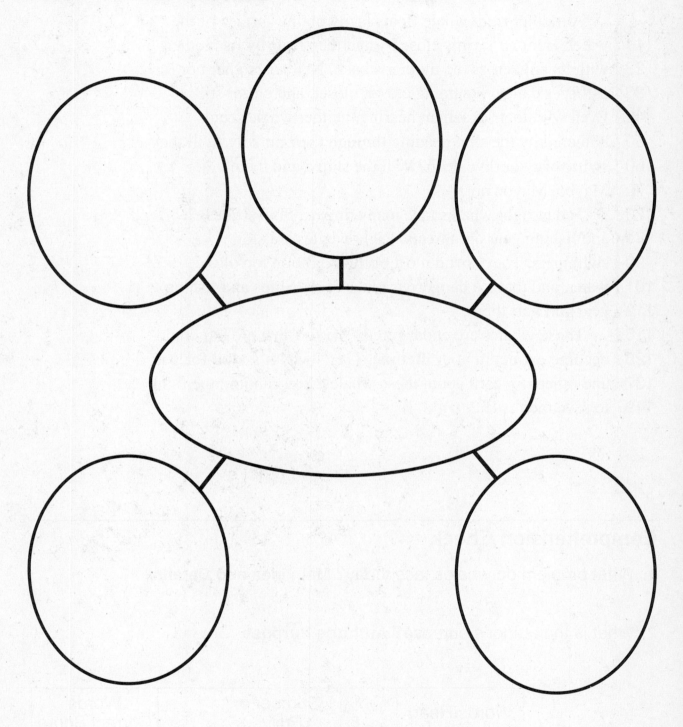

How does the information you wrote in this Main Idea Web help you make inferences and analyze the story structure of *Interrupted Journey*?

At Home: Have the student use the chart to retell the story.

Name _____

As I read, I will pay attention to tempo.

	A mother right whale floats lazily on the surface of the
11	water. Her calf swims close by and then rests by its mother
23	with its tail across the mother's back. Neither mother nor
33	calf sees danger steaming closer, closer, and closer still.
42	Even with their excellent hearing, neither whale seems
50	bothered by the ship heading through their nursery. Will they
60	swim away or dive deep? Will the ship avoid them?
70	Maybe. Maybe not.
73	Today right whales face many threats. Ship strikes
81	and fishing gear are threats. Right whales are slow
90	swimmers. They spend most of their days on top of the
101	water, and that's a dangerous place to be. Ships and fishing
112	gear can hurt them.
116	These whales are endangered. The few that are left could
126	become extinct in your lifetime. That's why it's **vital** for you
137	and others to learn about these whales. You can join the fight
149	to save them. 152

Comprehension Check

1. What problem do whales face today? **Main Idea and Details**

2. What is the author's purpose? **Author's Purpose**

	Words Read	–	Number of Errors	=	Words Correct Score
First Read		–		=	
Second Read		–		=	

 At Home: Help the student read the passage, paying attention to the goal at the top of the page.

Name _____

> **Alliteration** is the repetition of initial consonant sounds.
>
> **Imagery** is the use of words to create a picture in the reader's mind.

Read the poem. Then answer the questions.

> Lavender, lilac, azalea, lilies
> My butterfly garden grows.
> A shelter, sanctuary, haven, retreat
> Just as my home is to me.

1. What sound is repeated in the first line? In the third line?

_____

_____

2. What image is used in the poem? What picture comes to mind? _____

_____

_____

Think about an animal you would like to help protect. Write a free-verse poem about it. Be sure to include alliteration and imagery.

_____

_____

_____

_____

_____

_____

_____

_____

 At Home: Help the student write a short poem about an
animal that uses alliteration and imagery.

There are many ways to study words. One way is to identify the analogy relationships between pairs of words.

Analogies are written like this: up : down :: go : stop.
You read the analogy this way: "*Up* is to *down* as *go* is to *stop*."

Analogies sometimes use **antonyms** or opposites. *Up* and *down* are antonyms. *Go* and *stop* are antonyms, too.

To solve an analogy, identify the relationship between the first two words. Are they opposites or are they the same? If they are opposites, look for an antonym as the correct answer.

old : new :: open : _____

a. age   **b.** box   **c.** closed   **d.** buy

For this analogy, the correct answer is *closed.* The opposite of *old* is *new* and the opposite of *open* is *closed.* The correct answer choice is **c.**

Write the letter of the correct answer to finish the analogy.

1. healthy : sick :: tall : ____
   a. sorry   **b.** high   **c.** ill   **d.** short

2. go : come :: leave : ____
   a. walk   **b.** stay   **c.** run   **d.** away

3. negative : positive :: never : ____
   a. now   **b.** forever   **c.** always   **d.** early

4. simple : fancy :: hot : ____
   a. cold   **b.** meek   **c.** wet   **d.** burn

 At Home: Take turns finding antonyms for different words.

Name _____

Compound words are words that are made up of two or more words.

cup + cake = cupcake

When you find compound words, you can use the single words to help you pronounce the larger word. For example, look at the word *cupcake* above. First, you can figure out that the word is made up of two words, *cup* and *cake.* Now you can apply what you know about pronunciation to sound out the word. You know that the short *u* sound is often made by the letter *u* alone between two consonants. So you know how to pronounce *cup.* You also know that a vowel followed by a consonant and a silent *e* make a long vowel sound (VCe). So you know how to pronounce *cake.* Then put the two words back together again to pronounce *cupcake.*

Read each compound word below. Put a slash through the word to divide it into single words. Use what you know to sound out each separate word. Then put the two words together to pronounce the compound word.

1. anyone

2. blueberry

3. cornfield

4. everything

5. grandfather

6. anywhere

7. automobile

8. butterfly

9. gingerbread

10. snowstorm

 At Home: Help the student choose one of the words above and use it in a sentence.

A. Read each clue and select a vocabulary word from the box that means the same as the clue. Then write the word you selected on the line.

engulf	anxiety	cascade	foretold	remote

1. secluded _____

2. fearful concern _____

3. something falling or rushing _____

4. predicted _____

5. to flow over and enclose _____

B. Use the correct vocabulary words from the box below to complete the sentences below.

absorb	erode	pathetic	concentrated	generosity

6. Years of water and wind helped to _____ the rocks.

7. Jasmine showed a lot of _____ in her gifts to the other students.

8. A sponge is the best thing to use to _____ the spilled water.

9. Orange juice that has had all the water taken out is said to be

_____.

10. The food at the new restaurant was _____.

© Macmillan/McGraw-Hill

 At Home: Together write a paragraph using as many of the unit vocabulary words as possible.

Name _____

A. Choose a vocabulary word from the box to answer each question. Write your answer on the line provided.

| undetected | vital | speculated | scrounging | rummaged |

1. What do you call something of great importance? _____

2. What is something that is assumed to be true without complete proof?

   _____

3. What do you call something that is as yet undiscovered?

   _____

4. What is a word that means made a good search? _____

5. What word means to get what you need by begging or borrowing?

   _____

B. Use the correct vocabulary words from the box to make sense in the sentences below.

| propelled | dehydrated | ricocheting | chameleon | altered |

6. Many scientific discoveries have _____ the way people live and work.

7. The hikers did not bring enough water, and so they became

   _____.

8. Bouncing off of a surface, the ball was _____ around the room.

9. A lizard that can change the color of its skin is called a

   _____.

10. The train was _____ on the track by means of electricity.

At Home: Help the student write an antonym for the word *undetected.*

Name _____

| inscribed | resemblance | postmarked | enthralled |
| regulation | grouchy | embarrassment | pennant |

A. Write the letter of the definition beside each vocabulary word.

1. inscribed ____   **a.** the official one

2. resemblance ____   **b.** a state of feeling ashamed

3. postmarked ____   **c.** a similarity of appearance

4. enthralled ____   **d.** a flag or banner awarded for a championship

5. regulation ____   **e.** the official marking on a piece of mail

6. grouchy ____   **f.** to be spellbound by

7. embarrassment ____   **g.** In a bad mood, sulky

8. pennant ____   **h.** written or engraved

B. Choose four of the vocabulary words. Write a sentence using each of the words.

9. _____

_____

10. _____

_____

11. _____

_____

12. _____

_____

Name _____

Sometimes when you read, you can take clues the author gives you and make a good guess about something. This is called **making an inference.**

Read both sentences. Then make an inference and circle the letter of the correct answer for the blank in the second sentence.

1. Stacey and Ken ran out of paint before they finished the team banners.
   Stacey and Ken were _____ the team banners.
   a. buying   **b.** painting   **c.** finding

2. They had to stop working on the project because it was time for lunch.
   Stacey and Ken were working in the _____.
   a. morning   **b.** evening   **c.** afternoon

3. Stacey and Ken mixed together blue paint and yellow paint for the last banner.
   The last banner was painted _____.
   a. black   **b.** purple   **c.** green

4. Stacey is better at lettering than Ken or Ramon.
   _____ traced the letters on the banners.
   a. Ramon   **b.** Ken   **c.** Stacey

5. Everyone who saw the banners cheered and clapped.
   The banners were _____.
   a. ugly   **b.** beautiful   **c.** small

At Home: Take turns, writing a sentence like the clues above and making an inference from it.

Name _____

As you read *How Tía Lola Came to ~~Visit~~/Stay*, fill in the
Inferences Chart.

Text Clues and Prior Knowledge	Inferences

How does the information you wrote in this Inferences Chart help you
make inferences about *How Tía Lola Came to ~~Visit~~/Stay*?

 At Home: Have the student use the chart
to retell the story.

© Macmillan/McGraw-Hill

As I read I will pay attention to pauses, stops, and intonation.

	Eddie slams his math book closed and shoves it into his
11	book bag. He stuffs the last of his tortilla (tohr-TEE-yah)
21	into his mouth and jumps off of his bed. Then he picks up
34	the huge case that holds his accordion.
41	Eddie is careful with the case. This accordion is special.
51	It has been in his family for generations. First, Eddie's
60	grandfather played it, then Eddie's father, and now it belongs
70	to Eddie. The accordion is his prized possession.
78	Music has been a part of Eddie's family for generations.
88	The Hernandez family came to the United States from
97	Mexico, when Eddie's grandfather was a little boy. They
106	settled in San Antonio, Texas, where other Mexican families
115	had moved. Music often filled the air in the Close-knit
125	neighborhood.
126	Eddie's grandfather and father played in local bands.
134	Their bands played Tejano (te-HAN-oh) music. Tejano
141	means "Texan" in Spanish. 145

Comprehension Check

1. How can you tell that music is important to Eddie's community?
Make Inferences

2. What effect does music have on Eddie? What is the result? **Cause and Effect**

	Words Read	–	Number of Errors	=	Words Correct Score
First Read		–		=	
Second Read		–		=	

© Macmillan/McGraw-Hill

At Home: Help the student read the passage, paying
attention to the goal at the top of the page

How Tía Lola Came to ~~Visit~~/Stay

Grade 6/Unit 2

41

Name _____

An **almanac** is a book that is full of facts about things. You can find pictures of the flags of different countries or discover how many people live in Hartford, Connecticut. Almanacs are published yearly.

The index is the organizer for the almanac. Almanacs are also available online. Each entry is a link to the information you seek.

Use this partial almanac index to answer the questions that follow.

Animals   Energy   Flowers   Rain Forests
Architecture   Environment   Presidents, U.S.   ZIP codes
Brazil   First Ladies, U.S.

1. Under which two headings would you probably find information about Laura Bush? _____

2. Where would you look to find information about the vanishing rain forest in South America? _____

3. Where would you look to find part of an address for a university in Chicago, Illinois? _____

4. Where would you look to see who designed the White House?

   _____

5. Where would you look to find out about tulips?

   _____

 At Home: Together, think of other questions that could be answered by the almanac index at the top of the page.

Name _____

A verb in the past tense tells about an action that already happened. Add the **inflectional ending** -ed to most verbs to show past tense.

A. Add -ed to each of the following present-tense verbs.

1. play   _____

2. work   _____

3. hope   _____

4. paint   _____

5. help   _____

B. Now fill in the blanks in the sentences below with the correct past-tense verb from above. Use each verb only once.

6. Yesterday, Kelly and Ramon _____ the banners for the homecoming game.

7. Annelise has always _____ the goalie position on our soccer team.

8. Kelly said that she _____ hard on the banners.

9. Our teachers and the coach _____ we would win the game.

10. Ramon _____ Annelise practice blocking kicks.

At Home: Together, choose one verb from this page and write two sentences, one in the present tense without the -ed ending and one in the past tense with the -ed ending.

How Tía Lola Came to ~~Visit~~/Stay
Grade 6/Unit 2

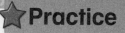
Write the plural of the following nouns.

- To form the **plural** of most nouns, add the letter -*s* to the end of the word. Example: bed, beds.
- To form the plural of nouns that end with a vowel and *o*, add -*s*. Example: rodeo, rodeos.
- To form the plural of nouns that end with a consonant and *o*, add -*s* or -*es*. Examples: concerto, concertos; potato, potatoes.
- To form the plural of some nouns ending in *f* or *fe*, change the *f* to *v* and add -*es*. Example: wolf, wolves.
- Some nouns have special plural forms, while others have the same singular and plural forms. Examples: goose, geese; salmon, salmon.

1. pet _____

2. cent _____

3. ratio _____

4. radio _____

5. photo _____

6. volcano _____

7. wife _____

8. knife _____

9. mouse _____

10. moose _____

© Macmillan/McGraw-Hill

At Home: Together, form the plural of the word *loaf* and write a sentence using the plural form.

| broadcast | vigil | marveled | spicy |
| unsatisfactory | undone | calculations | ravaged |

A. Write the letter of the definition beside each vocabulary word in column 1.

1. spicy ____   **a.** became filled with amazed curiosity

2. undone ____   **b.** not adequate

3. vigil ____   **c.** not finished

4. ravaged ____   **d.** the results of a mathematical process

5. marveled ____   **e.** destroyed by violence

6. broadcast ____   **f.** a period of watching

7. unsatisfactory ____   **g.** transmitted by radio or television

8. calculations ____   **h.** zesty; flavored with spices

B. Choose two vocabulary words. Write sentences using these words.

1. _____

_____

2. _____

_____

Name _____

> Sometimes readers must **make inferences**—conclusions based on evidence to fully understand a story.

Read the passage below. Then answer the questions. Make sure to identify the evidence that helped you to make the inference. You may underline the evidence in the passage.

Carla's father was tired. All day long, he had loaded boxes into the moving van. He had worked for the company for 20 years, and he usually enjoyed his work, but lately he had begun to regret the fact that he had not pursued his real love—music. He had always wanted to learn to play the piano.

"It is important for you to stay in school and get your education, like your brother Jorge did," Carla's father said to her. "Never give up on your dream to do the work you love best."

1. What type of company does Carla's father work for? _____

_____

2. What evidence led you to that inference? _____

_____

3. Is Carla's father satisfied with his work? _____

4. What evidence led you to that inference? _____

_____

5. Is Carla's brother older or younger than she is? _____

6. What evidence led you to that inference? _____

_____

7. Do you think Carla is likely to pursue her dreams? _____

8. What evidence led you to that inference? _____

_____

© Macmillan/McGraw-Hill

 At Home: Together, discuss inferences that you can make about some situations you know about.

As you read *The Night of the Pomegranate*, fill in the Inferences Diagram.

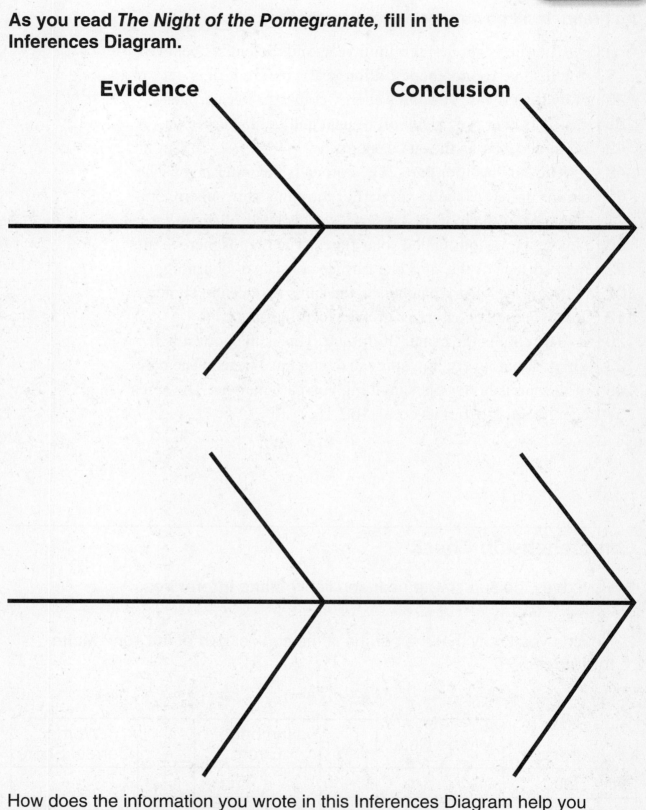

Evidence   **Conclusion**

How does the information you wrote in this Inferences Diagram help you monitor comprehension of *The Night of the Pomegranate*?

 At Home: Have the student use the chart to retell the story.

The Night of the Pomegranate
Grade 6/Unit 2 47

Name _____

As I read, I will pay attention to punctuation.

	The sun is about 4.5 billion years old. Scientists believe
9	it will shine for another 5 billion years, before it runs out
20	of hydrogen gas. The sun's energy comes from hydrogen
29	gas. This energy is given off as heat and light. All life on
42	Earth depends on the sun's energy.
48	The sun has four parts. The corona is the outer layer. The
60	chromosphere is the lower part of the sun's atmosphere, or a
71	layer of gas that covers the surface. This layer of gases has
83	violent explosions called solar flares. The photosphere is the
92	fiery surface of the sun. The surface consists of churning,
102	boiling gases. Dark patches on the sun's surface are cooler
112	areas. These cooler areas are known as sunspots.
120	The core is the center of the sun. This is the hottest part.
133	Think about a very hot, **spicy** dish you have tasted. The core
145	of the sun is hotter than anything you can imagine. The sun's
157	energy comes from its core. 162

Comprehension Check

1. How does the sun create heat and light? **Make Inferences**

2. How do you know that the corona is the coolest part of the sun? **Make Inferences**

	Words Read	–	Number of Errors	=	Words Correct Score
First Read		–		=	
Second Read		–		=	

48 The Night of the Pomegranate
Grade 6/Unit 2

At Home: Help the student read the passage, paying attention to the goal at the top of the page.

Name _____

Graphs show information visually. They are used to compare things or to show how things change over time.

The line graph below shows the number of nights Gregg went out star-gazing with his father from October through April of last year. Use the information in the line graph to answer the questions.

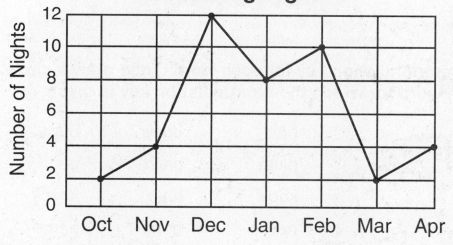

Star Gazing Nights

1. During which month did Gregg do the most star-gazing?

    _____

2. In which month did Gregg go star-gazing four times? _____

3. Between which two months was the greatest increase in star-gazing times?

    _____

4. What was the total number of star-gazing times between October and

    December? _____

5. What was the total number of star-gazing times for the months shown?

    _____

At Home: Ask the student to draw a line graph showing the number of times he or she performed some task for the seven days of a week.

The Night of the Pomegranate
Grade 6/Unit 2

You can check the dictionary to find out how to pronounce a word. You will find the **pronunciation key** right after the word in the dictionary. If you are unsure about the symbols in the pronunciation key, check the guide to pronunciation. The guide is found at the beginning of the dictionary, or sometimes at the bottom of each right-hand page. Look at the pronunciation key for this word:

tak´sē

The pronunciation key is for the word *taxi.*

Study the pronunciation key for each word. Then draw a circle around the word for which the pronunciation key is given.

1. **biz´ē**   bus   busy   buzz

2. **plum**   plum   plain   pen

3. **nok**   know   note   knock

4. **nun**   new   none   name

5. **sen´tər**   center   send   cent

6. **shō**   shore   shoe   show

7. **prə´nouns**   pronouns   pronounce   promote

8. **´re dē**   reader   red   ready

At Home: Together, look up the word *galaxy* in a dictionary and use the pronunciation key to pronounce the word.

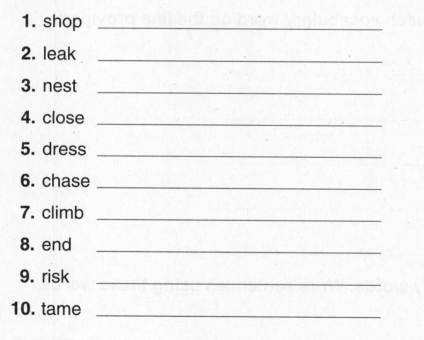
You know that when you add *-ed* or *-ing* to a word, you usually double the last consonant when the vowel that comes before it is a short sound.

hop + ed = hopped   hop + ing = hopping

Do not double the last consonant when the vowel sound that comes before it is long or when the word ends with more than one consonant. You just add the ending.

peek + ed = peeked   peek + ing = peeking

If a word ends with a silent *e* you drop the e before adding the ending.

time + ed = timed   time + ing = timing

Read each word quietly to yourself and listen to the way it sounds. Then add the endings *-ed* and *-ing* to each one. Follow the rules above.

1. shop _____

2. leak _____

3. nest _____

4. close _____

5. dress _____

6. chase _____

7. climb _____

8. end _____

9. risk _____

10. tame _____

 At Home: Ask the student to write words such as *beg* and *invent* and then add *-ed* and *-ing* to each.

Name _____

**A. Each underlined vocabulary word is shown in context.
Circle the clues that help you understand the word's meaning.**

1. Natural disasters such as hurricanes, tornadoes, and earthquakes are examples of <u>calamities</u>.

2. Volunteers offer people food, shelter, and water to try to <u>mitigate</u>, or lessen, their suffering.

3. The damage from an earthquake can be <u>devastating</u>, or incredibly destructive, to a community.

4. People near the coasts are encouraged to <u>evacuate</u>, or leave the area, when a hurricane is approaching.

5. Volunteers <u>administer</u>, or give out, food, water, and medical supplies when disaster strikes.

B. Write the definition of each vocabulary word on the line provided.

6. calamities _____

7. mitigate _____

8. devastating _____

9. evacuate _____

10. administer _____

C. Choose two vocabulary words. Write sentences using these words.

11. _____

_____

12. _____

_____

© Macmillan/McGraw-Hill

Name _____

A **generalization** is a broad statement based on a number of facts that you know. It does not include details that could be proved false. Generalizations often contain words such as *all, always, often, many, most, none, or least.* A good generalization cannot be proven false.

Write a generalization to answer each question. Use one of the following words to make each generalization: *all, always, often, many, most, none, or least.* Underline the word.

1. What generalization could you make about being prepared for an

    emergency? _____

    _____

    _____

2. What generalization could you make about when hurricanes strike?

    _____

    _____

3. What generalization could you make about the weather? _____

    _____

    _____

4. What generalization could you make about the basic things people need

    after a disaster? _____

    _____

    _____

At Home: Together, think about what your family can do to prepare for a natural disaster.

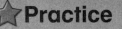
Name _____

As you read *Zoo Story*, fill in the Generalizations Chart.

Important Information	Generalization

© Macmillan/McGraw-Hill

How does the information you wrote in this Generalizations Chart help
you monitor comprehension of *Zoo Story*?

At Home: Have the student use the chart to retell the story.

As I read, I will pay attention to the pronunciation of vocabulary and other difficult words.

4	Officials at Bandelier (ban-duh-LEER) National Monument were afraid of wildfires. Bandelier is a national
13	park that lies near Los Alamos, a large town in New Mexico.
25	Park rangers did not want dry brush and grass in the park to
38	cause a wildfire. So they decided to start a planned fire.
49	Planned fires use up fuel like dry trees and brush that could
61	cause a wildfire.
64	But the fire quickly grew out of control. It became a
75	wildfire. High winds pushed flames in the direction of Los
85	Alamos. Los Alamos is an important town. It is home to the
97	Los Alamos Nuclear Laboratory. The laboratory built the
105	nation's first atomic bomb. The lab houses explosives and
114	other dangerous materials.
117	Los Alamos officials declared a state of emergency. All of
127	the town's residents had to **evacuate**. People who lived in
137	nearby towns had to leave, too. The laboratory needed to
147	act fast. Workers moved the explosive materials into
155	fireproof shelters. 157

Comprehension Check

1. Why is the western United States likely to have wildfires? **Make Generalizations**

2. What problem do park rangers face in a drought? How do they try to solve it? **Problem and Solution**

	Words Read	−	Number of Errors	=	Words Correct Score
First Read		−		=	
Second Read		−		=	

At Home: Help the student read the passage paying attention to the goal at the top of the page.

Zoo Story • Grade 6/Unit 2

A computer linked to the **Internet** can be used to find information that you need. Enter the keyword or keywords of a topic into the search box. Click on search. The search engine will bring up a list of Web sites related to your topic. Each link will have a brief description of its contents and an actual Web address. Read the descriptions to see which link best fits your need. Then click on the link.

A student searched the Internet to find organizations that helped people who survived the Indian Ocean tsunami. Use this search results list to answer the questions.

Sri Lanka Livestock **Relief** Fund for **Tsunami** Survivors...help Sri Lankan survivors of the **tsunami** buy livestock...http://www.srilankalivestockfund.org

Indonesian Homes for Homeless **Tsunami** Survivors...homeless Indonesians want disaster **relief** to rebuild...http://www.rebuildindonesia.org

Indian Communities 2004 **Tsunami** Emergency **Relief**...Indian communities affected by the tsunami...http://www.indiantsunamirelief.org

1. What does the first Web site tell you about? _____

_____

2. Which key words did the student use to find this Web site? _____

_____

3. If you want to find out about Indian communities after the tsunami, which

Web site would you click? _____

_____

4. What do you expect to read about if you click on the link Indonesian Homes

for Homeless Tsunami Survivors? _____

_____

At Home: Together, do an Internet search on relief efforts for a recent natural disaster.

© Macmillan/McGraw-Hill

When you read a paragraph, you may come across unfamiliar words. Use **context clues** within the paragraph to help you understand these words.

Read the paragraph. Find context clues to help you figure out the meanings of the underlined words and circle the clue. In the chart below, write your own definition for each underlined word.

Books by Disaster Help contain much needed information. For example, Disaster Help teaches the importance of preparing a disaster kit. The kit should contain <u>essential</u> medications. These are the medications that are absolutely necessary for the person. Disaster Help also <u>recommends</u>, or advises, that the kit contain a flashlight and <u>additional</u> batteries. These extra batteries will come in handy when the electricity fails to <u>function</u>. Batteries can power radios as well as flashlights when the power does not work.

	WORD	MY DEFINITION
1.	essential	
2.	recommends	
3.	additional	
4.	function	

Now choose one word and use it in a sentence of your own.

5. _____

_____

At Home: Together, write a sentence using the word *calamity* and a context clue to help define it.

Name _____

The spellings *ou, oi, au,* and *oo* can stand for different sounds.
For example:
- The *ou* in *sound* is different from *ou* in *fought*. The *ou* in *fought* stands for the same sound as the *au* in *taught*.
- The *oo* in *room* stands for a short *u* sound in the word *book*.
- The *oi* sound is the most regular. The *oi* in *boil* and the *oy* in *toy* stands for this sound.

1. Draw a circle around the words that have the same vowel sound as *taught*.

   laugh   bought   caught   could

2. Draw a circle around the words that have the same vowel sound as *room*.

   gloom   look   book   zoom

3. Draw a circle around the words that have the same vowel sound as *round*.

   taught   fought   sound   found

4. Draw a circle around the words that have the same vowel sound as *launch*.

   laugh   sauce   bunch   tune

5. Draw a circle around the words that have the same vowel sound as *house*.

   touch   loose   mouse   blouse

6. Draw a circle around the words that have the same vowel sound as *moon*.

   moose   caboose   pounce   lunch

7. Draw a circle around the words that have the same vowel sound as *spoon*.

   scoop   foot   boot   spot

8. Fill in each blank with *oi* or *oy* to spell a word.

   t_____   b_____l   sp_____l

At Home: In a newspaper or magazine, find two words with the vowels *ou* or *au* together, and ask the student what vowel sound is made by the letters.

© Macmillan/McGraw-Hill

Name _____

> coincidences   sweeten   phase   hobbled
> sheepishly   prospered   sumptuous   mufflers

Look at each definition below. Find the vocabulary word that fits the definition in the rows of letters after it. Draw a circle around the vocabulary word.

1. the quality of being extremely rich and magnificent
   t h e f a b r i c f o r t h i s g o w n i s r e a l l y s u m p t u o u s

2. accidental events that seem to be connected
   w e r e t h e s e e v e n t s r e a l l y j u s t c o i n c i d e n c e s

3. a part of a course of development
   i s t h i s a p h a s e y o u a r e g o i n g t h r o u g h

4. walked unsteadily
   t h e o l d m a n h o b b l e d a l o n g t h e u n e v e n p a v e m e n t

5. scarves
   i t w a s s o c o l d t h e s k i e r s w o r e m u f f l e r s

6. succeeded
   t h e d a u g h t e r o f t h e k i n g p r o s p e r e d i n t h e
   n e x t k i n g d o m

7. to make more attractive
   c a n y o u s w e e t e n t h e d e a l a l i t t l e b i t m o r e

8. showing embarrassment
   t h e b a d l i t t l e p u p p y l o o k e d a t m e s h e e p i s h l y

Name _____

Knowing how to identify the **problem** a character has and paying attention to how she or he finds a **solution** will help you better understand and enjoy a story. Look at the following sentences:

The old king does not want his daughter to move far away after she marries.

   The **problem** is that the king does not want his daughter to move far away after she gets married.

   The king's **solution,** or answer, to the problem, is to find his daughter a prince who lives nearby.

Read each problem below. Then describe the character's solution for each problem as you remember it from the story.

1. **Problem:** The miller's daughter doesn't know how to spin straw into gold.

   Solution: _____

2. **Problem:** The miller's daughter now must spin more gold. If she doesn't, she dies. If she does, she has to marry the king.

   Solution: _____

3. **Problem:** Rumpelstiltskin's daughter must figure out a way to satisfy the king and help the poor farmers and hungry children.

   Solution: _____

4. **Problem:** Rumpelstiltskin's daughter realizes the king wants more and more gold.

   Solution: _____

   _____

At Home: Together, write about a problem the student has helped to solve.

As you read *Rumpelstiltskin's Daughter,* fill in the
Problem and Solution Chart.

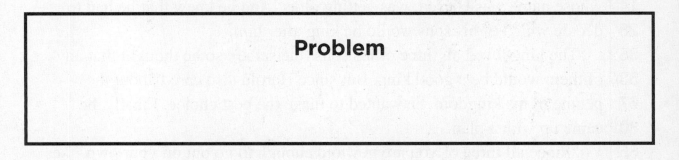

Problem

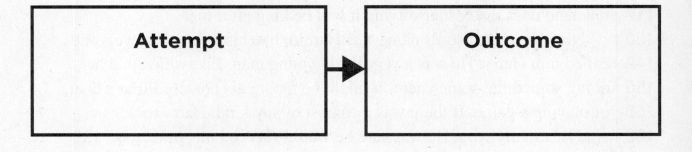

Attempt → **Outcome**

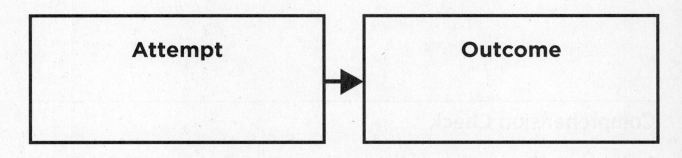

Attempt → **Outcome**

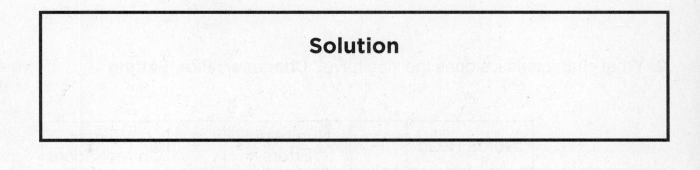

Solution

How does the information you wrote in this Problem and Solution Chart
help you monitor comprehension of *Rumpelstiltskin's Daughter*?

 At Home: Have the student use the chart to retell the story.

As I read, I will pay attention to tempo.

14	Once, long ago, there was a great king who had three sons. The king, whose name was Harold, was getting older. And he knew that he had to
28	decide which of his sons would be king after him.
38	The king loved all three of his sons (the same), so he thought that any
53	of them would be a good king. But since Harold also cared about the
67	people of his kingdom, he wanted to make the best choice. Finally, he
80	came up with a plan.
85	"Since all three of you are now old enough to go out on your own," he
101	told his sons one day, "I will give you a problem for you to solve. The
117	one who does the best at solving it will be king after me."
130	Now, the oldest son's name was Harold, like his father, but everyone
142	called him Harry. He was a very lively young man. Every day he'd be
156	doing something somewhere. It might be racing his horse, sailing a boat,
168	or playing a game. If there was a contest of any kind, Harry took part.
183	And he usually won. He was sure he would succeed this time, too. 196

Comprehension Check

1. What is the king's problem? What is his solution? **Problem and Solution**

2. What characteristics does the king have? **Character, Plot, Setting**

	Words Read	–	Number of Errors	=	Words Correct Score
First Read		–		=	
Second Read		–		=	

 At Home: Help the student read the passage, paying attention to the goal at the top of the page.

© Macmillan/McGraw-Hill

A myth is a story that is told over and over. Myths often explain things that happen in nature through the help of gods and goddesses.

A **moral** is a practical lesson that you can learn by reading a myth.

Hyperbole is the deliberate use of exaggeration for emphasis. Myths often use hyperbole to describe human weaknesses.

Read the following myth. Then answer the questions.

Many years ago, Moon did not have the dark spots on his face that he has today. His face was shining and beautiful. Moon was a huge silvery ball in the sky and he was quite vain about his looks. Moon was so bright that he could be seen not only at night but all day long. Sun, who warmed the earth and all its people, became jealous of Moon. Why did her people spend their long sunny days gazing at themselves in the silvery surface of Moon? Sun saw her people becoming vain, lazy, and conceited. She decided to solve the problem by giving Moon big ugly craters in his face. Finally, Sun ruled that Moon's ugly face would be seen only at night.

1. What facts of nature does this myth explain? _____

_____

_____

2. What is the moral? _____

_____

_____

3. How is hyperbole used in this myth? _____

_____

_____

4. What are some other myths that you know about? _____

_____

_____

 At Home: Together, make up a myth to explain why rain falls.

Rumpelstiltskin's Daughter
Grade 6/Unit 2

 63

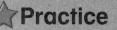
Name _____

When you hear someone say, "It's raining cats and dogs," it does not mean that cats and dogs are falling from the sky. This expression is an example of an **idiom.** An idiom is a group of words that together mean something different from the meaning of each individual word. You can use context clues to help you figure out the meaning of an idiom. You can also check the dictionary to help you understand the expression. Often, the dictionary explains how the main word is used in the context of a popular idiom.

Use context clues or the dictionary to help you figure out the meaning of the following idioms. First, underline the idiom. Then write what it means in the space provided. Consult a dictionary if you need to.

1. The town mayor is still thinking about building us a skateboard park. We

   wish she would make up her mind. _____

   _____

2. Last week Maria lost her homework and forgot her lines in the school play. But today Maria found out she made the soccer team. Things are really

   looking up for Maria. _____

   _____

3. Jackson ran the fastest mile, jumped the highest in the high jump, and cleared every hurdle in the last track meet. I think that Jackson has team

   captain in the bag. _____

   _____

4. Margie finished all the grocery shopping and decorated the house. She completed all the cooking this afternoon. Margie is really on the ball.

   _____

   _____

© Macmillan/McGraw-Hill

At Home: Together, find the meaning of this idiom: Did Terrence <u>get wind of</u> the party plans?

Name _____

You can break large words into syllables by looking at letter patterns. Figure out how to pronounce the syllables before blending them together.

When you have a word with a Vowel Consonant Consonant Vowel (**VCCV**) pattern, you can draw a line between the two consonants to break up the word.

Example: surface   sur/face

Sometimes words will have two sets of VCCV patterns, as in important.   im/por/tant

If you find a word with a Vowel Consonant Consonant Consonant Vowel (**VCCCV**) pattern, insert the syllable break between the consonant and the blended consonants.

Example: shuffle   shuf/fle

Look at the words below. Copy the words on the lines provided and draw a line to break the words into syllables.

1. picnic _____

2. table _____

3. apartment _____

4. mountain _____

5. children _____

6. mitten _____

7. muffler _____

8. panther _____

At Home: Together, break the following word into a VCCV pattern: *slipper.*

Rumpelstiltskin's Daughter
Grade 6/Unit 2

65

Name _____

A. Each underlined vocabulary word is shown in context in the following passage. Circle the context clues for the underlined words.

Dan looked for the animal hospital just outside, or on the <u>outskirts</u>, of the town. Dan's sick dog, Topper, was in <u>quarantine</u>, or separated from healthy animals. Dan had agreed to <u>intercept</u>, or take possession of, the medicine Topper needed to get well. He waited to allow the <u>pedestrians</u>, or people on foot, to cross the street. The <u>plight</u>, or dangerous situation of the dogs, was known by the entire community. There was an <u>epidemic</u>, a rapid outbreak of disease, among the sled dogs. Dan had agreed to a <u>rendezvous</u>, a meeting, with the veterinarians at the animal hospital. The fact that his dog was sick was <u>unbearable</u>, or extremely hurtful, to Dan.

B. Write the definition of each vocabulary word on the line provided. Use the context clues you circled above.

1. outskirts _____   5. plight _____

2. quarantine _____   6. epidemic _____

3. intercept _____   7. rendezvous _____

4. pedestrians _____   8. unbearable _____

C. Choose two vocabulary words and write sentences for them.

9. _____

_____

10. _____

_____

Events in a story happen in a certain order or **sequence.**
Understanding the sequence of events can help you better
understand what you read.

**A. Read each description below of an event from _The Great Serum_
Race. The events are listed out of sequence. Number the events
in the order in which they happened as you remember the story.**

____ A doctor in Anchorage packs a supply of diphtheria serum
for the long journey.

____ One month after the epidemic began, the quarantine is lifted and the
whole town celebrates.

____ Twenty brave mushers and more than 160 brave dogs carry the serum
across the frozen trails of Alaska from Anchorage to Nome.

____ Dr. Welch discovers a case of diphtheria in Nome, Alaska.

____ The serum is given to the sick children and lives are saved.

**B. Use the space below to draw a picture of something that
happened in the story.**

At Home: Choose a favorite book or movie plot and
have the student verbally tell you the events of the
plot in sequence.

The Great Serum Race
Grade 6/Unit 2

67

As you read *The Great Serum Race,* fill in the Sequence Chart.

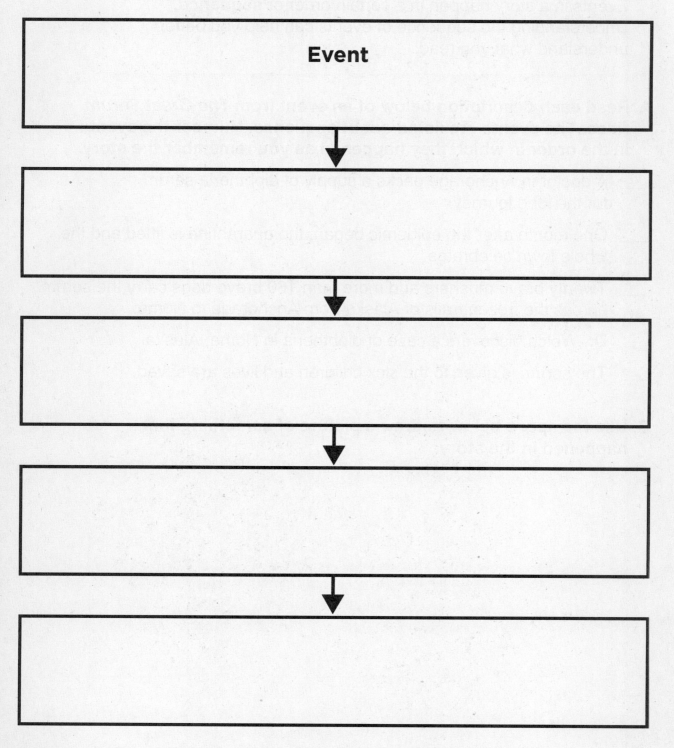

Event

How does the information you wrote in this Sequence Chart help you monitor comprehension of *The Great Serum Race*?

 At Home: Have the student use the chart to retell the story.

© Macmillan/McGraw-Hill

As I read, I will pay attention to pronunciation of vocabulary words and context clues.

	The first rescue dogs started out as fierce animals trained
10	to fight in war. About 2,000 years ago, armies from Rome
20	invaded the land that is now Switzerland. To get there, they
31	crossed the Alps, a snowy mountain range. The Romans
40	brought along large dogs.
44	High in the Alps, Roman dogs watched out for enemies
54	along the mountain passes, or roads. When the soldiers
63	returned home, they left some of their dogs behind.
72	Some wealthy landowners kept them as watchdogs.
79	Perhaps it was one of these landowners who first gave some
90	of the dogs to the monks who lived high in the Alps at the
104	Hospice of St. Bernard.
108	A monk named Father Bernard built the Hospice in
117	the year 1049 as a safe place for **pedestrians** to stay as
129	they traveled over the dangerous mountains. As they hiked
137	up and down the steep mountain, people had to worry about
148	robbers. They also faced snowstorms and avalanches. The
156	monks rescued travelers from such **plights**. 162

Comprehension Check

1. What events lead to Father Bernard obtaining the dogs? **Sequence**

2. What problem did people face in the Alps? What was Father Bernard's solution? **Problem and Solution**

	Words Read	–	Number of Errors	=	Words Correct Score
First Read		–		=	
Second Read		–		=	

At Home: Help the student read the passage, paying attention to the goal at the top of the page.

Haiku is a form of Japanese poetry. It is usually three lines long. The first line has five syllables; the second, seven; the third, five. Haiku often describes something in nature.

Symbolism is the use of an everyday thing to stand for something more meaningful.

Metaphor is a comparison of two essentially unlike things.

Read the haiku. Then answer the questions.

> Bright, white, cold, clean snow---
> Begin again, a new day,
> Quiet, clear, icy.

1. What everyday thing is used as symbolism in the poem? _____

_____

_____

2. What two essentially unlike things are compared in the poem? What is this

comparison called? _____

_____

_____

Write a haiku of your own. You may "paint of picture" of a winter scene, or any other season. Include a symbol and a metaphor.

_____

_____

_____

At Home: Together, write a five-syllable first line for a haiku and challenge the student to write the remaining two lines.

© Macmillan/McGraw-Hill

Name _____

> Words that have the same or nearly the same meanings are called **synonyms**. *Slim* and *slender* are synonyms. You can use synonyms to help you figure out the meaning of unfamiliar words. Often, synonyms are used as context clues. Look at this example of a synonym used as a context clue:
>
> The reward for the hero sled dogs was abundant, or plentiful, food.
>
> In this sentence, *plentiful* is a synonym for *abundant*.
> Dictionaries often include synonyms for words. A special kind of dictionary called a **thesaurus** always lists synonyms.

A. Use a dictionary or a thesaurus to find a synonym for each of the following words.

1. nourish _____

2. evident _____

3. obligation _____

4. surplus _____

B. Choose one of the words above. Write a sentence using it. Then replace the word with the synonym you listed. Make sure the meaning of the sentence does not change.

5. _____

_____

_____

_____

 At Home: Discuss a synonym for the verb *persuade.*

You can break words into smaller parts, called syllables, by looking at letter patterns. When you have a word with a Vowel Consonant Vowel (**VCV**) pattern, you can divide it in two different ways.

- If the vowel before the consonant is long, the break comes after the vowel, as in mu/sic. It follows the **V/CV** pattern. It is the most common pattern.
- If the vowel before the consonant is short, the break comes after the consonant, as in clos/et. It follows the **VC/V** pattern.
- If the first syllable is unstressed, as in a/gain, the break comes after the unstressed vowel. It follows the **V/CV** pattern.

A good way to find where the word should break is to sound out the syllables, using first the long and then the short vowel sounds. The pronunciation that sounds right and the **VCV** patterns will help you find the correct word and the correct syllables.

Look at the words below. Copy the words on the lines provided and draw a line to break the words into syllables.

1. about _____

2. shovel _____

3. patience _____

4. woman _____

5. aboard _____

6. hoping _____

7. balance _____

8. around _____

At Home: Together, break the following word into a VC/V pattern: *shadow*.

© Macmillan/McGraw-Hill

Name _____

A. Read each clue and write a vocabulary word from the box on the line.

| inscribed | regulation | vigil | broadcast | evacuate |

1. to leave the area _____

2. a period of watching _____

3. written or engraved _____

4. the official one _____

5. transmitted by radio or television _____

B. Use the correct vocabulary words from the box to complete the sentences below.

| mitigate | administer | phase | sumptuous | mufflers |

6. Grandma always prepares a _____ feast for Grandpa's birthday.

7. Janice knit everyone on the ski team extra-warm _____.

8. We hope our new puppy's chewing is just a brief _____.

9. The volunteers did all they could to _____ the effects of the disaster.

10. The doctor will _____ the flu shots to everyone in line.

A. Choose a vocabulary word from the box to answer each question. Write your answer on the line provided.

unbearable	intercept	plight	sheepishly	administer

1. What is another word for a dangerous situation? _____

2. What is a synonym for take possession? _____

3. What do you call something that is extremely hurtful? _____

4. What is a word that means to show embarrassment? _____

5. What word means to give out? _____

B. Use the correct vocabulary words from the box to make sense in the sentences below.

spicy	ravaged	calculations	grouchy	resemblance

6. Pauline always seems to be in a _____ mood.

7. The strawberry fields were _____ by the hurricane.

8. We made the chili extra _____ this time.

9. The _____ proved the team could afford new uniforms.

10. The _____ between the two red-haired girls was remarkable.

© Macmillan/McGraw-Hill

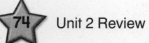

Name _____

A. Each underlined vocabulary word is shown in context in the following sentences. Circle the context clue that explains the underlined word.

1. Esmerelda hoped the tomatoes would <u>flourish</u>, or grow very well.

2. The <u>foreman</u>—the person in charge of the workers—showed Esmerelda how to plant them.

3. Esmerelda's father was an <u>employee</u>, or worker, at the farm.

4. Esmerelda wanted to <u>fulfill</u>, or meet, her father's expectations.

5. She spent hours in the kitchen, <u>gleefully</u> chopping tomatoes and onions with high-spirited joy.

6. Esmerelda <u>gloated</u> about her victory and took exceptional pride in her skills.

7. She <u>vigorously</u> scrubbed the dishes, forcefully and energetically washing the pots and pans.

8. Esmerelda <u>gritted</u> her teeth, grinding them together as she scrubbed.

B. Write the definition of each vocabulary word on the line provided. Use the definition from the sentences above if necessary.

9. flourish _____

10. foreman _____

11. employee _____

12. fulfill _____

13. gleefully _____

14. gloated _____

15. vigorously _____

16. gritted _____

Every story has certain elements, or standard items. The **characters** are the people that the story is mostly about. The **setting** is where and when the story takes place. The **plot** is the series of events that make up the story.

Mateo was a skilled actor. He had won many awards for young actors, and he liked to boast of his acting skills. One day at home Mateo sat down in a chair to read a newspaper. When he started to stand up, he found that he couldn't move. Upon this discovery, he began to panic.

"What if I can't ever act again?" he thought to himself. "What will I do with myself? My days will seem endless!"

He sat there, thinking these thoughts until his mom walked in the door. "Mom!" he exclaimed. "Help me, I'm paralyzed and I can't get up!" His mom walked over and pulled him to his feet. "Mateo, you're a very talented actor, but sometimes you have no common sense. You're not paralyzed! You were sitting on a piece of gum! Look, the chair is just stuck to you!"

"Oh," said an embarrassed Mateo. "I was just practicing a new role. If I can convince you, then I know I will be able to convince an audience!"

Write the answer to each question in the story map below.

MAIN CHARACTERS

1. _____   2. _____

SETTING

3. _____

PLOT

4. _____

_____

_____

_____

 At Home: Together, read and discuss the characters, setting, and plot of a favorite story.

As you read *Juan Verdades,* fill in the Summary Chart.

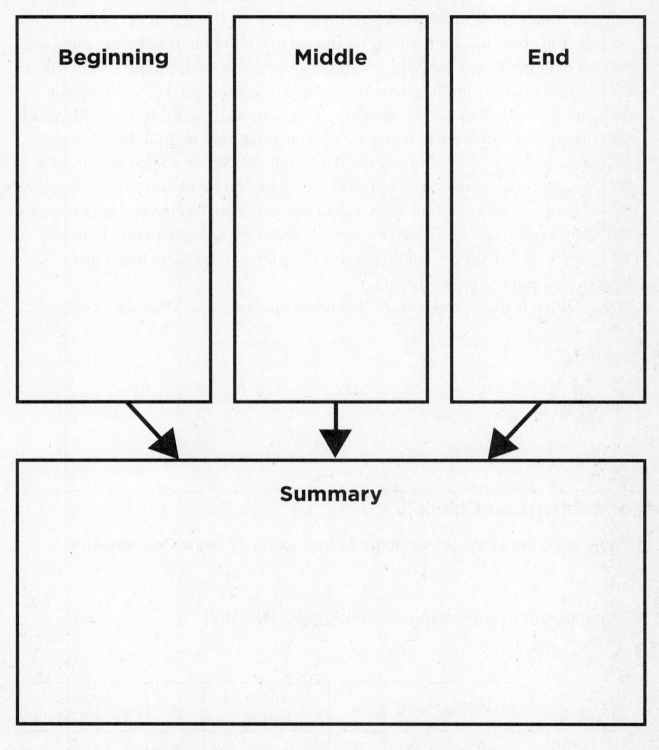

Beginning	Middle	End

Summary

How does the information you wrote in this Summary Chart help you monitor comprehension of *Juan Verdades*?

At Home: Have the students use the chart to retell the story.

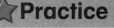
Name _____

As I read I will pay attention to pauses stops and intonations.

	What is gold's true worth?
5	You could ask John Sutter. He moved to California in 1839, his mind set
18	on building a huge farming enterprise. Sutter constructed a fort, collected
29	12,000 head of cattle, and hired hundreds of **employees**. He sent **foreman**
40	James Marshall to build a sawmill on the American River. In 1848, Marshall
52	discovered they were erecting the mill on a rich vein of gold. It was the
67	greatest find in the history of the West. And yet, Sutter wanted no part of it.
83	What he wanted most was to **fulfill** his dream and build his farming business.
97	But when word of the gold leaked out, suddenly fortune seekers overran
109	California. They trespassed on Sutter's holdings, and eventually destroyed
118	his dream. To Sutter, that dream was his gold, not the shiny metal that
132	glinted and winked in the sun.
138	What is gold's true worth? You could also ask Josie Montana. 149

Comprehension Check

1. Why does the story ask what gold's true worth it? **Draw Conclusions**

2. What turn of events changed John Sutter's life? **Plot**

	Words Read	−	Number of Errors	=	Words Correct Score
First Read		−		=	
Second Read		−		=	

© Macmillan/McGraw-Hill

 At Home: Help the student read the passage, paying attention to the goal at the top of the page.

Name _____

Maps are pictures or charts showing the features of an area. A road map like the one below will help you get to a place by car. A political map shows the boundaries of countries or states. Still others, such as a topographical map, show high places, like mountains, and lower places, like valleys.

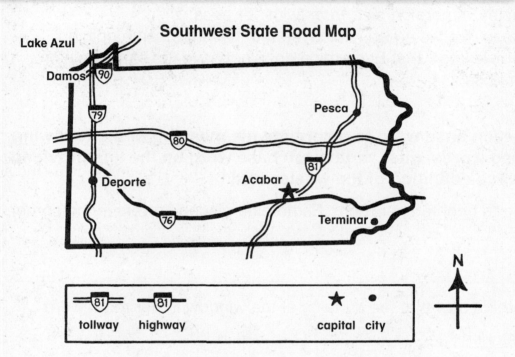

Southwest State Road Map

This is a map of a fictional state called "Southwest State." Use the map to answer these questions.

1. What city is the capital of Southwest State? _____

2. What kinds of roads are shown on the map? _____

_____

3. If you were in Deporte, which highway would take you to Damos?

_____

4. If you drove from Acabar to Pesca, would you pay a toll? Explain. _____

_____

5. What city is almost directly north of Terminar? _____

 At Home: Together, use a road map to trace the route from your home to school.

Name _____

Some words may have as many as three parts: a prefix, a **base word**, and a suffix or inflectional ending. Look at the word *disagrees.* The base word, *agree,* gives the heart of the word's meaning. If you can identify and understand the base word, you can use your knowledge of its meaning to figure out the meaning of the entire word.

Example: Esmerelda *disagrees* with her boss.

The base word is *agree,* which means "have the same opinion as." So we know that Esmerelda does not have the same opinion as her boss.

Identify each base word to determine the meaning of the following underlined words. First, write each base word on the line provided. Then write a definition of the whole word.

1. Hoping to <u>brighten</u> her room, Esmerelda placed flowers in the corner.

   _____

   _____

2. Esmerelda saw that the curtains at the window in her room were

   <u>mismatched</u>. _____

   _____

3. Esmerelda <u>misplaced</u> her measuring spoon. _____

   _____

4. Mr. Valdez took an <u>interstate</u> road to the next state capital.

   _____

   _____

5. Shannon's face showed her impatience and indignation._____

   _____

© Macmillan/McGraw-Hill

At Home: Have the student identify and define the base word in *unteachable.*

Name _____

An **accented** syllable is one that is pronounced a little louder, with a little more stress. Say these two words to yourself: *almost, again*. In *almost*, the accent is on the first syllable: AL-most. In *again*, the accent is on the second syllable: a-GAIN. Figure out which syllable is accented in this word: *morning*. The first syllable is accented: MORN-ing.

If you were to look in a dictionary for the correct pronunciation of these words, the accented syllable would have a boldfaced stress mark before it. It looks like this: 'morn-ing.

A. Say each word out loud. If the first syllable is accented, as in the word *almost*, write 1. If the second syllable is accented, as in the word *again*, write 2.

1. birthday ____

2. after ____

3. about ____

4. airplane ____

5. balloon ____

6. parade ____

7. children ____

8. money ____

9. alone ____

10. tonight ____

B. Choose two of the words above. Write a sentence for each word.

11. _____

_____

12. _____

_____

At Home: Help the student identify the accented syllable in five two-syllable words.

Juan Verdades • Grade 6/Unit 3

Name _____

| embarked | promenade | unimaginable | sensational |
| limousine | extravagant | lamented | precarious |

A. Write the letter of the correct definition beside each vocabulary word.

1. embarked ____

2. promenade ____

3. unimaginable ____

4. sensational ____

5. limousine ____

6. extravagant ____

7. lamented ____

8. precarious ____

a. a large, luxurious vehicle

b. to express regret

c. a leisurely walk

d. characterized by a lack of stability

e. arousing a superficial interest

f. not conceivable

g. lacking in restraint

h. started

B. Choose two vocabulary words. Write sentences using these words.

9. _____

_____

10. _____

_____

© Macmillan/McGraw-Hill

> A **conclusion** is an opinion or a decision you can reach based
> on information provided by the author, as well as what you know
> from your own experience.

Read each passage. Then fill in the chart.

Inez has been hired to write "human interest" stories for the *River City Times* newspaper. This will be Inez's first job. She didn't sleep at all the night before her first day of work.

What I Know	Information from Story	Draw Conclusions
People can be nervous the first day on a new job.		

Marty and I have been friends since kindergarten. One day I borrowed his inline skates and left them at the skating rink. I went back to search for them, but they didn't turn up. I don't want to lose Marty's friendship.

What I Know	Information from Story	Draw Conclusions
Marty and I have been friends for a long time. I lost his skates, but I don't want to lose his friendship.		

© Macmillan/McGraw-Hill

 At Home: Together, discuss the emotions involved
in preparing for a big event.

Nothing Ever Happens on 90ᵗʰ Street
Grade 6/Unit 3

Name _____

As you read *Nothing Ever Happens on 90th Street,* fill in the Conclusions Chart.

What I Know	Text Evidence	Conclusions

© Macmillan/McGraw-Hill

How does the information you wrote in this Conclusions Chart help you monitor comprehension of *Nothing Ever Happens on 90th Street?*

 At Home: Have the student use the chart to retell the story.

As I read I will pay attention to punctuation.

	"We have to do something," said Lisa. She gave her four
11	friends a look that showed she meant business. Then she
21	stared at the newspaper article again and frowned. Lisa was
31	a girl who usually had a smile on her face and a great idea in
46	her mind. But today nobody was smiling.
53	Lew, Kelsey, Nina, and Cory nodded, but nobody spoke
62	for a long time. Silence seemed to envelop them, and it was
74	not a comfortable silence but an eerie one.
82	In one night, their lives were abruptly and completely
91	changed. When the storm began, everyone had raced home,
100	but nobody was yet worried. After all, what harm could a
111	little rain and wind do? Certainly nothing significant.
119	The wind grew stronger by the hour. The five friends had
130	constantly called each other to check that everyone was all
140	right. At one point, Cory and Lew were talking on the
151	telephone when the telephone suddenly went dead. Then the
160	lights went out, all over Maple Grove. 167

Comprehension Check

1. What event changed the lives of Lisa and her friends? **Draw Conclusions**

2. How do you know that Lisa will develop a plan? **Make Inferences**

	Words Read	–	Number of Errors	=	Words Correct Score
First Read		–		=	
Second Read		–		=	

At Home: Help the student read the passage, paying attention to the goal at the top of the page.

An interview follows a pattern of **questions** and **answers**. To get the answers you want, you need to ask questions in the right way. Use the following guidelines for interviewing.
- Write your questions before the interview.
- To start the interview, state what you hope to find out.
- Remember that your job is to listen, not talk.
- Take notes, during the interview. If possible, record the interview so that you can listen again to the information.
- Ask follow-up questions to get more information.
- Review your notes or tapes soon after the interview.

Read the interview format below. Then answer the questions.

Subject: Tasha Washington, author of *The Long Road Home*
Purpose: to find out about Mrs. Washington and her new book
Questions:
1. Tell me about your education. How did it prepare you for your career?
2. When and how were you first published? Tell me about your first publication. Tell me about your new book.

1. What is the purpose of the interview? _____

_____

2. What follow-up question does the reporter ask about Tasha's education?

_____

_____

3. What is the name of Tasha's book? _____

_____

4. If you were to interview Tasha, what is one question you would ask?

_____

_____

© Macmillan/McGraw-Hill

At Home: Have your student list people he or she would like to interview, and why.

Dictionaries provide readers with the history, or origin, of a word. The **word's origin** usually comes after the pronunciation key and the identification of its part of speech. Some common abbreviations are Ar: Arabic; ME: Middle English; F: French; ML: Medieval Latin; L: Latin; Gk: Greek.
Study the word *algebra,* a kind of mathematics, and its origin.
algebra \'al-jə-brə\ *n (*ML fr Ar al-jabr, lit. the reduction)
You can read the dictionary abbreviations above as "Medieval Latin from Arabic, *al-jabr,* the reduction."

Use a dictionary to find the origins of the following words. Write down the earliest origin listed in the dictionary.

1. book _____

2. colony _____

3. violin _____

4. dentist _____

5. proof _____

6. dollar _____

7. coffee _____

8. nice _____

9. imperial: _____

10. giraffe _____

© Macmillan/McGraw-Hill

At Home: Together, use a dictionary to find the origin of the word *Earth.*

Nothing Ever Happens on 90th Street
Grade 6/Unit 3

Name _____

The ə is common in English. Any vowel, *a, e, i, o,* or *u,* can stand for the ə in a word. Sometimes, the ə at the end of a word, followed by the consonant *r.* The words *racer, doctor,* and *regular* are examples of this.

Read the following sentences. Write the words that contain ər on the line. Underline the letters that stand for _ər_.

1. Mother and father came to hear me read my poetry this week.

_____

2. I wrote another poem just the other morning.

_____

3. Even my brother thought this new poem was better.

_____

4. My poems express similar thoughts and themes.

_____

5. One day I hope to be a director, producer, or actor.

_____

6. I am planning to be an author when I grow up.

_____

7. Emily drank some ginger tea to calm her stomach.

_____

8. As a lawyer, Gretchen helped people who needed legal advice.

_____

At Home: Together, underline all the words that have the ər sound in a newspaper article or magazine page.

Name _____

A. Each underlined vocabulary word is shown in context in the following sentences. Circle the context clue that gives the definition of the underlined word.

1. Some sources of energy are <u>nonrenewable</u>; they cannot be made again.

2. Other sources of energy are <u>renewable</u>; we are able to find them over and over, like the sun, wind, and water.

3. An <u>adverse</u> effect is a negative effect.

4. When you <u>generate</u> energy, you make or produce it.

5. On the roof of our home, there is an <u>apparatus</u>, or machine, for making solar energy.

B. Write the definition of each vocabulary word on the line provided. Use the definitions from the sentences above if necessary.

6. nonrenewable _____

7. renewable _____

8. adverse _____

9. generate _____

10. apparatus _____

C. Choose two vocabulary words and write sentences for them.

11. _____

12. _____

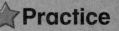
Name _____

When you read, look for cause-and-effect relationships. A **cause** is the reason something happens. The **effect** is the result of the cause. Look at the following sentences:

- The Bloom family tries to buy only what they need. As a result, they save money, energy, and natural resources.
- The cause is that the Bloom family buys only what they need.
- The result, or effect, is that they save money, energy, and natural resources.

Authors use words like *as a result, so, therefore, because, due to, then,* and others to show these cause-and-effect relationships.

Read the following sets of sentences. Sometimes the cause is mentioned first, and sometimes the effect is mentioned first. Underline the cause and circle the effect.

1. Ted Bloom knows that if he makes fewer purchases, then there will be less to throw away.

2. Ted also buys things that can be reused. The result is that he saves the energy needed to make new things.

3. Ted recycles all the materials that he can because recycling materials uses less energy than making new ones.

4. Hannah has been swimming and lifting weights because she wants to be more fit.

5. As a result of his love of reading, Miguel became an editor.

6. Due to a mix up at the office, Maya was not enrolled.

© Macmillan/McGraw-Hill

 At Home: Together, list ways your family can reduce, reuse, and recycle.

Name _____

As you read *Building Green,* fill in the Cause and Effect Chart.

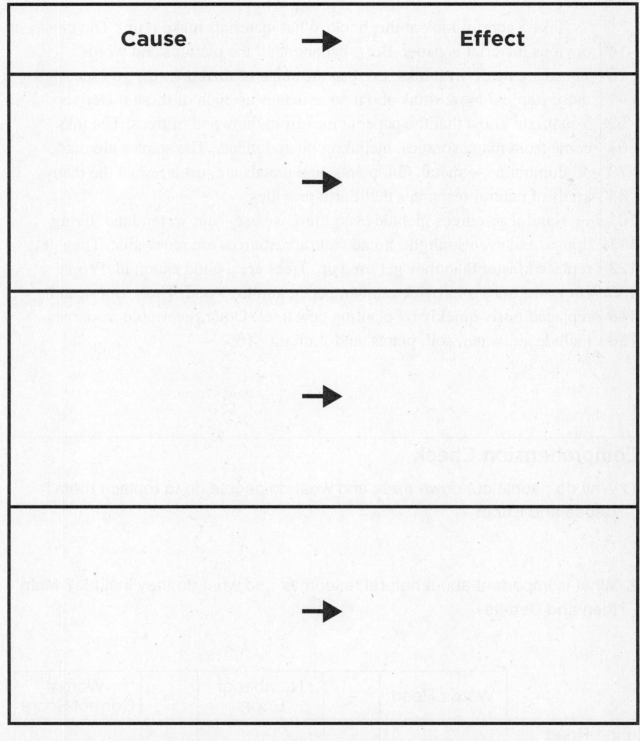

Cause	→	Effect
	→	
	→	
	→	

How does the information you wrote in this Cause and Effect Chart help
you monitor comprehension of *Building Green*?

 At Home: Have the students use the chart to retell the story.

As I read I will pay attention to the pronunciation of vocabulary and other hard words.

	Take a careful look at this book. What materials make it up? The most
14	obvious material is paper. But what about all the pictures and words?
26	Those are made with inks. Look at the spine of the book. Do you see
41	those staples? Now, think about what makes up each of these materials.
53	You might know that the paper comes from the wood of trees. The inks
67	come from many sources, including oil and plants. The staples are made
79	of aluminum—a metal. Oil, plants, and metals are just a few of the many
94	kinds of natural resources that Earth provides.
101	Natural resources include everything we use—air, water, land, living
111	things, and even sunlight. Some natural resources are renewable. They get
122	replaced faster than they get used up. Trees are a good example. People
135	cut down trees to provide lumber, paper, and firewood. Those trees can be
148	replaced fairly quickly by planting new ones. Other renewable resources
158	include air, water, soil, plants, and sunlight. 165

Comprehension Check

1. Why do people cut down trees and what do people do to replace them? **Cause and Effect**

2. What is important about natural resources and what do they include? **Main Idea and Details**

© Macmillan/McGraw-Hill

	Words Read	−	Number of Errors	=	Words Correct Score
First Read		−		=	
Second Read		−		=	

At Home: Help the student read the passage, paying attention to the goal at the top of the page.

Study Strategies make your work easier.

Skimming material means you look over material to get a general idea of what it is about. Do not read every word. Look at headings, boldfaced words, italicized terms, pictures, and other items that stand out.

Scanning material means you think of some key words and read quickly to find those words. This often leads you to some useful information.

Taking notes helps you remember important facts and details. Write down important dates and terms. If you make your notes on index cards, you can organize them easily.

Outlining the main idea and the supporting details helps you master information. Use a formal outline or an informal one.

Choose a chapter or section from your social studies or science book. Use the techniques listed above. Then make an outline in the space below.

_____

_____

_____

_____

_____

_____

_____

_____

_____

_____

_____

_____

At Home: Together, find a good place for the student to work. Encourage good study strategies as outlined on this page.

Name _____

Use the words that are nearby an unknown word to give you clues to the word's meaning. A context clue can state the definition, or meaning, of the unknown word in the same sentence. Sometimes the general context of the sentence will give you a clue to the word's meaning. Find the context clue in this sentence:

• Architects, the people who design buildings, often try to find new ways to save energy.

The context clue tells you that *architects* are "people who design buildings."

Use the context clues to help you figure out the meaning of each underlined word below. Write the meaning on the line.

1. The big <u>dispute</u> in our town went on and on in an endless argument about how to save energy.

_____

2. Ted Bloom tried to be <u>impartial</u>, but it was difficult to be fair and objective about something that meant so much to him.

_____

3. Jeremiah was in favor of <u>promoting</u> the use of renewable resources, since encouraging these kinds of resources could save energy.

_____

4. Jeremiah did not want to <u>squander</u> or waste energy in any way.

_____

5. "We need more <u>efficient</u> ways to create energy," Jeremiah said, "because the less energy we waste now, the more we will have in the future."

_____

At Home: Together, find the context clue in this sentence: "We must preserve the homes, the natural <u>habitats</u>, of endangered animals."

© Macmillan/McGraw-Hill

Name _____

The /ə/ sound appears in unaccented syllables. The symbol for this sound is called a schwa. It can appear at the end of multisyllable words, such as *-en* or *-on* words with the /ən/ sound, and *-el, -le* , and *-al* words with the /əl/ sound.

A. Fill in the correct letters to make the final /ən/ sound in the following words.

1. drag _____

2. fright _____

3. happ _____

4. wag _____

B. Fill in the correct letters to make the final /əl/ sound in the following words. Then write the complete word on the line.

5. hand _____

6. squirr _____

7. doub _____

8. buck _____

C. Draw a circle around the words that follow the spelling patterns that make the /ən/ and the /əl/ final sounds.

9. I need one nickel more to buy the flannel shirt I want.

10. Open the door a little more and see what will happen.

11 Paul wanted to level the requirements so everyone could take part.

12. Patrick had proven us wrong, but he was gracious about it.

13. Tyra used pliers to tighten the bolts on her skates.

14. Max had a dimple that showed when he smiled.

At Home: Together, find all of the words in a newspaper article that have the *ən* and *əl* sounds.

Name _____

A. Each vocabulary word is shown in context in the following sentences. Circle the context clue that helps you determine the underlined words' meaning.

1. Archaeologists are usually not <u>superstitious</u>; they do not have fears of the unknown.

2. Sometimes archaeologists study highly advanced, or <u>civilized</u> societies.

3. To <u>prolong</u> an archaeological dig is to lengthen it in time.

4. Usually things found deeper in the earth <u>precede</u>, or come before in time, those that are found higher up.

5. Archaeologists often find <u>trenches</u>, or irrigation ditches.

6. The young archaeologist was firm in her determination, <u>steadfastly</u> digging at the site.

7. She wanted to <u>excavate</u>, or dig up, the ancient kitchen before the sunset.

8. She found a complete set of <u>utensils</u>, tools still useful today for kitchen use.

B. Write the definition of each vocabulary word on the line provided.

9. superstitious _____

10. civilized _____

© Macmillan/McGraw-Hill

When you **summarize** a story, you use your own words to briefly tell the most important ideas or events in that story.

Summarize each paragraph below in a sentence.

1. Do you enjoy reading about ancient cultures? Do you like visiting museums? Do you like to like to look for arrowheads? If so you may want to become an archaeologist.

   Summary: _____

   _____

2. Archaeologists must dig for artifacts gently and carefully. They must also take detailed notes and make sketches. Sometimes they spend years trying to solve a mystery. Patience is helpful.

   Summary: _____

   _____

   _____

3. Archaeologists must read about ancient cultures. They must also learn the language. They have to write research papers.

   Summary: _____

   _____

4. Archaeologists do not just dig. Some teach university classes. A few create museum exhibits. Others work for the government.

   Summary: _____

   _____

   _____

At Home: Together, watch a television show or read a short story and summarize the events.

The Emperor's Silent Army
Grade 6/Unit 3

97

Name _____

As you read *The Emperor's Silent Army*, fill in the Summary Chart.

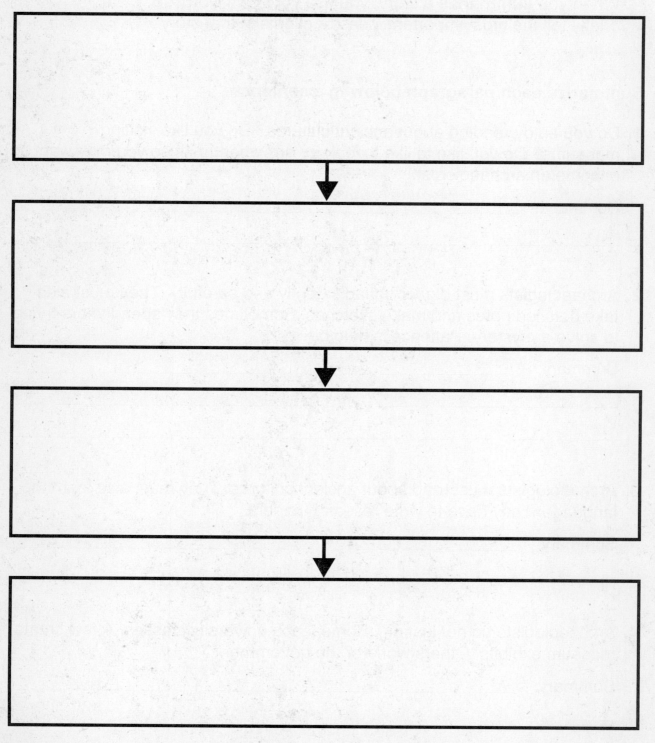

How does the information you wrote in this Summary Chart help you
monitor comprehension of *The Emperor's Silent Army*?

 At Home: Have the student use the chart to retell the story.

© Macmillan/McGraw-Hill

Name _____

As I read, I will pay attention to tempo or expression.

	Ancient myths and legends tell the stories of powerful gods and kings.
12	One ancient Greek myth tells the story of King Minos (MIGH-nohs).
22	King Minos ruled his kingdom from the city of Knossos (NOHS-us)
32	on the island of Crete. The legend says he kept a terrible monster locked
46	up in an underground labyrinth, or maze. This monster was half-man
57	and half-bull. It was called the Minotaur (MIN-uh-tohr). Every year, the
67	city of Athens had to send young men and women to Crete as sacrifices to
82	the Minotaur.
84	Stories of King Minos and his fabulous palace were told in Ancient
96	Greece and the stories never entirely disappeared. Many people
105	**steadfastly** believed the city of Knossos existed. They thought it had
116	been built on Kephala (KAY-fah-lah), a hill on Crete's northern coast. But
127	nobody knew for sure if there really had been such a place or even a king
143	named Minos. 145

Comprehension Check

1. How would you describe the legend of King Minos? **Summarize**

2. Why do you think people believed that Knossos existed? **Draw Conclusions**

	Words Read	−	Number of Errors	=	Words Correct Score
First Read		−		=	
Second Read		−		=	

At Home: Help the student read the passage, paying attention to the goal at the top of the page.

Meter is the rhythmical pattern of unstressed and stressed syllables in a line of poetry.

In the line of poetry below, the stressed syllables are in capital letters and the unstressed syllables are in lowercase letters. Read the line softly to yourself, placing the emphasis where Longfellow intended it.

TELL me / NOT in / MOURNful / NUMbers,

LIFE is / BUT an / EMPty / DREAM.
　　　　　　　　　　—Henry Wadsworth Longfellow

Consonance is the repetition of final consonant sounds in two or more words grouped together. For example: *Hear the roar of tigers near.*

Read the following poem by Emily Dickinson, "The Bee is Not Afraid of Me." Then answer the questions.

　　The Bee is not afraid of me.
　　I know the Butterfly.
　　The pretty people in the Woods
　　Receive me cordially —

　　The Brooks laugh louder when I come —
　　The Breezes madder play;
　　Wherefore mine eye thy silver mists,
　　Wherefore, Oh Summer's day?

1. Find examples of consonance in the poem.

_____

2. Rewrite the final line of the poem, using capital letters for the stressed syllables and lowercase for the unstressed.

_____

At Home: Together, read a poem aloud. Discuss the poem's meter, any alliteration or consonance, and its meaning.

Name _____

Prefixes are attached to the beginnings of words and often change the words' meanings. Look at the following chart of prefixes and their meanings.

Prefix	Meaning	Example
un- *il-* *dis-*	not, without, the opposite of	unhappy illegal disappear
re-	do again	retype
super- *extra-*	beyond or above	superhuman extraordinary
anti-	against	antibacterial antilock
mis-	badly, poorly, not	mismatch

Write the meaning of each word. Use your knowledge of prefixes to help you define the words.

1. extrasensory: _____

2. rewrite: _____

3. misbehave: _____

4. discomfort: _____

5. antifreeze: _____

 At Home: Have the student add a prefix to the word *place* and use it in a sentence.

The Emperor's Silent Army
Grade 6/Unit 3

Name _____

Prefixes are added at the beginning of words. They usually change the word's meaning. If you do not know the meaning of the word with its prefix, try to think of another word with the same prefix that you do know.

For example, you might know that a *bicycle* has two wheels, so the word *bimonthly* could mean two times a month or every two months.

A. Read each word below and make an educated guess about its meaning, using what you know about prefixes. Write the meaning of the word on the line. You can use a dictionary to check your work.

1. illegal _____

2. biplane _____

3. tricycle _____

4. untrue _____

5. supervise _____

B. Use some of the prefixes used in 1–5 to make up some words of your own. Write the words and their meanings on the lines.

6. _____

7. _____

8. _____

At Home: Together look through a newspaper or magazine. Identify and define two words with prefixes.

Name _____

A. Read the following sentences and fill in the blank with a vocabulary word.

sponsoring	array	significance	charismatic
mimics	despondently	sleuthing	anonymous

1. The hardware store is _____ our community theater.

2. The manager showed us an _____ or collection of theater props.

3. I did not understand the _____ or importance of props and sets.

4. I thought _____ or charming actors were all that was needed!

5. Brandon imitates or _____ the great actors of the 1930s.

6. She spoke _____, as if she had given up hope.

7. Amanda goes _____ at yard sales, searching for old movie posters.

8. Celebrities sometimes wish they could remain unknown, or

   _____ actors.

B. Choose two vocabulary words and write sentences for them.

9. _____

   _____

10. _____

   _____

A **conclusion** is an opinion or a decision you reach based on information provided by the author, as well as what you know from your own experience.

Read the story. Then fill in the chart.

At first Stevie was disappointed that she didn't get the lead in the new production of *Kiss Me, Kate.* But Mrs. Gruber encouraged her to work with the crew backstage instead of quitting in a sulk. So Stevie began working with the carpenters to build the set. She also helped paint the scenery. She spent an afternoon in antique stores hunting for just the right props. And finally, since she was an expert seamstress, Stevie volunteered to make the beautiful lavender silk gown for the final scene. When people applauded at the end of the play, Stevie came onstage with everybody else and took a bow.

What I Know	Information From Story	Draw Conclusions
Stevie was disappointed that she didn't get the part.		
Stevie is very talented in many ways.		

At Home: Together, discuss the importance of contributing to an event "behind the scenes."

© Macmillan/McGraw-Hill

Name _____

**As you read *The Case of the Phantom Poet,* fill in the
Conclusions Chart.**

Text Clues	Conclusion

How does the information you wrote in this Conclusions Chart help you
monitor comprehension of *The Case of the Phantom Poet?*

At Home: Have the student use the chart to retell the story.

The Case of the Phantom Poet
Grade 6/Unit 3

105

As I read, I will pay attention to dialogue, tempo, and intonation.

	Later that morning, at Frankie's school.
6	*Frankie and Michael stand on the sidewalk. Frankie*
14	*waves to everyone and speaks in her new voice.*
23	FRANKIE: Hi, how are you! Hi, there, I'm Frankie
32	Smithers, and I'm new in town!
38	MICHAEL: Stop using that weird voice.
44	FRANKIE: I'm being friendly. I'm letting them know that
53	Frankie Smithers has moved to town!
59	MICHAEL: You're scaring them–and me. Listen, Frankie,
67	drop the act, and just be yourself.
74	FRANKIE: I am being myself. I am confident, and I am
85	eager to meet new people!
90	MICHAEL: And I'm eager to be leaving you.
98	*(Michael leaves. Frankie approaches Principal Ben Rojo.)*
105	FRANKIE: Good morning! You must be the principal!
113	*(Natalie walks by. She smiles at Frankie.)*
120	PRINCIPAL ROJO: Frankie, this is Natalie Benton. She'll
128	be in your homeroom. Natalie, this is–
135	FRANKIE: Frankie Smithers, and I love to play basketball!
144	*(to the principal)* Natalie and I are old friends! 153

Comprehension Check

1. Why do you think Frankie is trying to change herself? **Draw Conclusions**

2. Why does Frankie's brother tell her to be herself? **Make Inferences**

	Words Read	–	Number of Errors	=	Words Correct Score
First Read		–		=	
Second Read		–		=	

 At Home: Help the student read the passage, paying attention to the goal at the top of the page.

Name _____

Tables organize and present information in a way that is quick and easy to read. This table presents information about what's playing at two community theaters.

Play	Theater	Dates
The Glass Zoo	Cook Theater	March 1–15, 2006
Beauty and the Bats	Ashland Theater	March 3–12, 2006
The Lion Emperor	Cook Theater	March 16–31, 2006
The Tempest	Ashland Theater	March 13–31, 2006

Use the table to answer the questions.

1. How many shows are listed? ____

2. Which play is opening March 16? _____

3. Where is *The Tempest* being staged? _____

4. Which play is being performed at the Cook Theater on March 4?

_____

5. Which play is closing March 12 at the Ashland Theater?

_____

At Home: Together, look in the newspaper and find the time, place, and date of a movie.

The Case of the Phantom Poet
Grade 6/Unit 3

Name _____

> **Synonyms** are words that have the same or nearly the same meaning.
> Analogies can help you identify the relationships between pairs of words such as synonyms.
> Analogies are written like this: baby : infant :: happy : joyful.
> Read the analogy like this:
> "Baby is to infant as happy is to joyful."

Study the relationship between the first two words of each of the following analogies. Circle the letter of the correct answer.

1. frequent : often :: rare :
   a. seldom **b.** much **c.** usual **d.** useful

2. radiant : glow :: silence :
   a. bright **b.** noise **c.** quiet **d.** sun

3. fresh : new :: stale :
   a. bread **b.** old **c.** original **d.** darken

4. rapid : quick :: slender :
   a. fast **b.** growth **c.** height **d.** slim

5. brave : bold :: powerful :
   a. strong **b.** foolish **c.** reckless **d.** courage

6. conflict : disagreement :: applaud :
   a. yell **b.** praise **c.** argument **d.** approach

At Home: Have the student give a synonym for the word *craft*.

You can use words that you already know to build new vocabulary and improve your spelling. For instance, you can change some verbs to nouns by **adding** a form of the **-ion** or **-ation** ending. To change the verb *educate* to a noun, drop the last *e* and add *-ion* for *education*.

Sometimes because of the way the word sounds you have to use the alternative ending *-ation,* as in *admiration.* This form of the ending uses the long *a* sound.

A good test for which ending to use would be to see if you can pronounce the word with the *-ion* ending. *Admirion* is hard to say, so we use the *-ation* ending for *admiration.*

A. Read each verb and decide which ending you should use to change it to a noun. Try out the *-ion* ending first. If that does not sound correct, then use *-ation.* Write your nouns on the lines that follow each base word.

1. contribute _____   3. decorate _____

2. demonstrate _____   4. observe _____

B. Use each of your nouns in sentences of your own.

5. _____

_____

6. _____

_____

7. _____

_____

8. _____

_____

© Macmillan/McGraw-Hill

At Home: Together, look through a newspaper or magazine and find words with an *-ion* or *-ation* suffix.

The Case of the Phantom Poet
Grade 6/Unit 3

109

A. Choose a vocabulary word from the box to answer each question. Write your answer on the line provided.

flourish	employee	fulfill	vigorously	embarked

1. What is another word for *worker*? _____

2. What is another way to say *energetically*? _____

3. What is another way to say *grow very well*? _____

4. What word means *meet the requirements*? _____

5. What word means *started*? _____

B. Use the vocabulary words from the box to complete the sentences.

promenade	extravagant	lamented	adverse	generate

6. Alex's Thanksgiving meals are always _____.

7. We took a relaxing _____ on the boardwalk.

8. Our solar panels will _____ electricity.

9. We hope no _____ weather ruins our vacation.

10. Alex _____ that he didn't win the contest.

Name _____

A. Match each vocabulary word with the letter of the correct definition.

1. apparatus ____   **a.** tools for kitchen use

2. precede ____   **b.** lengthen in time

3. utensils ____   **c.** belief in chance

4. superstitious ____   **d.** come before

5. prolong ____   **e.** machine or device

B. Write sentences using the vocabulary words from the box.

| steadfastly   sponsoring   array   significance   anonymous |

6. _____

7. _____

_____

8. _____

_____

9. _____

_____

10. _____

_____

Name _____

A. Each underlined vocabulary word is shown in context in the following sentences. Circle the context clue of the underlined word.

1. Sun-Mi and her hiking partners climbed to the <u>summit</u>, or highest point, of the mountain.

2. The view from the mountaintop was <u>awesome</u>—truly extraordinary.

3. Danny's hiking team included a number of <u>specialists</u>, or people with specific skills.

4. Cody noticed how the little house on the mountain had <u>deteriorated</u> and become rundown.

5. Zoe was an experienced hiker, known among her friends as having a great deal of <u>maturity</u>—she seemed to have fully grown qualities.

6. Benjamin often offered <u>guidance</u>, or advice, to young hikers.

7. Justin told hikers to always use their <u>peripheral</u> vision on the mountain, to look to the sides and not just straight ahead.

8. Shelby also warned, "There is no <u>typical</u> day on the mountain. Expect the unusual, not the usual."

B. Write the definition of each vocabulary word on the lines below.

9. summit _____

10. awesome _____

© Macmillan/McGraw-Hill

 At Home: Choose two vocabulary words to use in a sentence.

An **author's purpose** for writing is usually to entertain, persuade, or inform.

Read each paragraph below. Then write the author's main purpose.

1. In 1943 Ansel Adams photographed Japanese Americans interned during World War II. Over two hundred of these photographs will be on display at the Center City Museum from April 1 through July 31.

Author's Purpose: _____

2. Namiko plays the cello. When she flies to concerts in other cities, she always books a seat next to her for her cello. Often Namiko has a difficult time getting her cello aboard the plane. Once a customer service agent told her, "I need to see Cello's driver's license, please."

Author's Purpose: _____

3. Victoria is hearing impaired, but it does not keep her from competing in rodeos. She wants to raise money so that she can compete in several rodeos. Will you help Victoria reach her goal by purchasing a raffle ticket?

Author's Purpose: _____

4. To make brownies, you should combine 2 cups of flour, 1 teaspoon of baking powder, and 1 cup of sugar in a bowl. In a saucepan, heat 2 chocolate squares and 1 stick of butter until they are melted. Pour the melted mix into the bowl. Add 2 eggs and mix all the ingredients in the bowl. Heat the oven to 350°. Pour the mix into a baking pan. Bake for 30 minutes.

Author's Purpose: _____

At Home: Together, write a story to inform, entertain, or persuade.

As you read "Seeing Things His Own Way," fill in the Author's Purpose Chart.

Clues	Author's Purpose

How does the information you wrote in this Author's Purpose Chart help you monitor comprehension of "Seeing Things His Own Way"?

Seeing Things His Own Way
Grade 6/Unit 4

At Home: Have the student use the chart to retell the story.

114

As I read, I will pay attention to pauses, stops, and intonation.

	Philip Wrigley came up with an idea. He would start a
11	women's professional softball league. Though the idea of
19	women playing professional sports is not unusual today, it
28	was not **typical** in 1940. In fact, in 1940, professional
36	options for women were very limited. Only about one
45	quarter of American women had jobs outside the home.
54	But soon women would begin to take on the jobs of
65	men who left to fight the war. Ready or not, the times
77	were about to change.
81	With men fighting in the war, the country had no choice
92	but to allow women to work and do new things. Wrigley
103	thought it was the perfect time to sell the idea of a women's
116	softball league.
118	Baseball teams were scrambling for new players to fill in
128	for their missing all-stars. Many major league teams were
137	in trouble. There were fewer games. It looked as if baseball
148	might shut down entirely until the war was over. As men's
159	baseball **deteriorated**, Wrigley asked major league
165	ballparks to host women's teams. They all said no. 174

Comprehension Check

1. Why does the author present opinions about women from the 1940s?
Author's Purpose

2. What problem did the war create for baseball. What was the effect?
Problem and Solution

	Words Read	−	Number of Errors	=	Words Correct Score
First Read		−		=	
Second Read		−		=	

At Home: Help the student read the passage, paying attention to the goal at the top of the page.

Seeing Things His Own Way
Grade 6/Unit 4

115

Name _____

A **diagram** is a drawing that explains how something works or how to do something. Diagrams often have **labels** identifying their parts.

Study the diagram of a school auditorium. Then use the information in the diagram to answer the questions below.

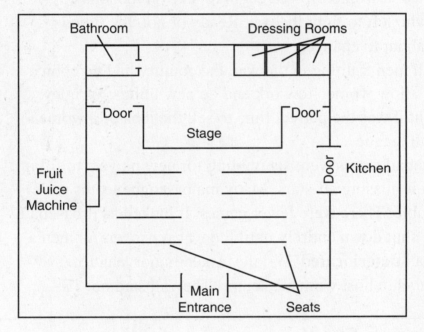

1. If you walked through the main entrance, what would be directly in front of you? _____

2. Where is the bathroom located? _____

3. How many doors are there to the kitchen? _____

4. How would you get behind the stage? _____

_____

5. Where is the fruit juice machine? _____

 At Home: Together, draw a diagram of a room in your home, showing furniture, doors, and windows.

© Macmillan/McGraw-Hill

Name _____

> **Synonyms** are words that have similar meanings. When you see
> an unfamiliar word, look for context clues. Sometimes a synonym
> for the word will be in the same sentence or paragraph.

**Read the sentences. Fill in the blank with a possible synonym for
the underlined word.**

1. Melanie warned her fellow hikers not to <u>stray</u> off the trail. It was not safe to

   _____ off alone in the mountains.

2. Courtney wanted to <u>ascend</u> the cliff face first thing in the morning. She liked

   more than anything to _____ at daybreak.

3. The system of ropes was <u>complex</u>. Zach explained to the young climbers

   that they would need lessons to master the _____ system.

4. The belt Andy wore when he climbed was not <u>ornamental</u> or

   _____. It was an important part of his safety equipment.

5. Ryan did not like to be <u>bothered</u> or _____ during a climb. Any
   distraction could slow a climber.

6. Alicia was <u>tired</u> and _____ after climbing all day.

7. Nathan was <u>passionate</u> about rock climbing. His _____
   infected us all even though our muscles were sore.

8. Makayla was the first to reach the <u>summit</u>. We have a photo of her at the

   _____ of the mountain.

At Home: Together, find synonyms for words
in a book chapter.

Name _____

> The suffix *-ion* changes a verb to a noun. In many cases you can just add the ending, as in *act + ion = action.*
>
> You usually drop a silent *e* from the end of the base word when you add the ending, as in *create + ion = creation.*
>
> Sometimes you change the spelling at the end of the base word to make the new word easier to say.
>
> Examples:
>
> the letters *de* become an *s*, as in *divide + ion = division*;
>
> the letter *t* becomes *ss*, as in *permit + ion = permission*;
>
> the letters *eive* become *ept*, as in *perceive + ion = perception*

Add the *-ion* suffix to each of the following words. Make any spelling changes you need. Consult a dictionary if you are unsure of the new word's spelling.

1. abbreviate _____

2. attract _____

3. distinct _____

4. elect _____

5. omit _____

6. edit _____

7. elect _____

8. intersect _____

9. pollute _____

10. produce _____

 At Home: Together, use each word pair above in a sentence.

Name _____

| formations | wreckage | intact | severed |
| interior | hovering | edgy | clockwise |

A. Read the following sentences. Each underlined word is a vocabulary word. Use the sentences to help you define the word.

Seeing coral underline{formations}, or arrangements, was Pete's favorite part of scuba diving. Sometimes he saw the <u>wreckage</u> of old rowboats on the floor of the ocean. Often, the inside of a sunken cabin cruiser was still <u>intact</u>. Sometimes, though, the top part of the boat was <u>severed</u> from the bottom part. Pete had been warned not to swim into the <u>interior</u> of any sunken vessel. He often found himself <u>hovering</u> over a sunken ship. His diving partner became <u>edgy</u> whenever Pete mentioned exploring old wrecks. Pete always remembered to turn the handle on his oxygen tank in a <u>clockwise</u> direction.

B. Write the letter of the definition beside each vocabulary word in the first column.

1. formations ____   **a.** the inside

2. wreckage ____   **b.** tense, irritable

3. intact ____   **c.** broken parts

4. severed ____   **d.** the same way the hands of a clock move

5. interior ____   **e.** divided by cutting

6. hovering ____   **f.** in one piece

7. edgy ____   **g.** suspended over an object or place

8. clockwise ____   **h.** arrangements

C. Choose two vocabulary words. Write sentences using these words.

9. _____

_____

10. _____

_____

Facts are statements that can be proven true. **Opinions** are statements than cannot be proven true.

Each statement below is a fact or an opinion. If the statement is a fact, write *fact* on the line provided. If the statement is an opinion, write *opinion* on the line provided.

1. The ocean liner R.M.S. *Titanic* was built in 1911. _____

2. Many people thought the *Titanic* was "virtually unsinkable."

   _____

3. The ship struck an iceberg in 1912. _____

4. The Titanic was discovered on the floor of the ocean in 1985.

   _____

5. The wreckage of the *Titanic* was the most famous discovery in history.

   _____

6. Everyone thinks the *Titanic* disaster was tragic. _____

7. The movie about the *Titanic* disaster is the saddest movie ever made.

   _____

8. Many artifacts from the shipwreck are still in good condition.

   _____

 At Home: Together, write two more facts and two more opinions about the *Titanic*.

Name _____

As you read *Exploring the Titanic*, fill in the Fact and Opinion Chart.

Fact	Opinion

How does the information you wrote in this Fact and Opinion Chart help you monitor comprehension of *Exploring the Titanic*?

 At Home: Have the student use the chart to retell the story.

As I read, I will pay attention to punctuation.

	In 2002 Dr. Eugenie (yew-JEE-nee) Clark was teaching
6	a university class. Her students listened closely. Dr. Clark
15	was a leading expert on sharks and other fish. After a long
27	and happy career, it was her final class at the University of
39	Maryland.
40	After class, the students threw a farewell party. They
49	wanted to thank their teacher for inspiring them. Eugenie, or
59	Genie always had that effect on her students. And she
69	always had plenty of adventures to tell them about. Eugenie
79	Clark was more than a teacher. She was a world traveler, an
91	explorer, and a pioneer in women's undersea diving.
99	Genie Clark's love of the sea started early. Her whole
109	family loved going to the beach near their New York home
120	whenever they could. Genie's uncle would thrill her by
129	doing fancy dives.
132	Her mother was graceful and sure in the water. Genie
142	wanted to be just like her. She learned to swim and loved
154	being in the water. 158

Comprehension Check

1. Why is the statement "Eugenie or Genie always had that effect on her students" an opinion? **Fact and Opinion**

2. What events in Clark's childhood influenced her career? **Draw Conclusions**

	Words Read	−	Number of Errors	=	Words Correct Score
First Read		−		=	
Second Read		−		=	

Exploring the Titanic
Grade 6/Unit 4

122

At Home: Help the student read the passage, paying attention to the goal at the top of the page.

Hyperbole is the use of exaggeration for emphasis. Tall tales often include exaggerated details.
Dialogue is a conversation between two or more characters. It is usually set off by quotation marks.

Read the tall tale. Then answer the questions.

Rubber-Band Ruby was the toughest, smartest, most flexible woman in the state of Wyoming. Everyone for miles around knew about Ruby because of her amazing rubber-band arms. One day Ruby's Ma and Pa were having problems herding their cattle. They just couldn't seem to get those little doggies to round up right. Ruby said, "I'll round up those little doggies for you!"

Pa said, "Are you sure you can, Ruby?" Ruby just laughed and stretched her arms so far they reached all the way into South Dakota.

"I'll just put my arms around 'em and herd 'em in," Ruby said.

1. Who is the hero of the tall tale? _____

2. What problem does she solve in a funny way? _____
_____

3. What is exaggerated in the tall tale? What is this exaggeration called?
_____
_____
_____

4. Write a line of dialogue from the tall tale. _____
_____

5. Make up a line of dialogue to end the tall tale. _____
_____
_____

 At Home: Together, think of a name for the hero of a tall tale.

Suffixes are attached to the ends of words and often change the words' meanings. Look at the following chart of suffixes and their meanings.

Suffix	Meaning	Example
-dom -hood	state of, condition of	wisdom childhood
-er	a person who does something, a native of	baker southerner
-ment	means, result, action	refreshment
-ty	quality, state	beauty
-ant	actor, agent, showing	servant
-ous	marked by, given to	jealous

A. Write the meaning of each word. Use your knowledge of suffixes to help you define the words.

1. observant: _____

2. freedom: _____

3. disappointment: _____

4. novelty: _____

5. manager: _____

B. Make a word of your own by adding a suffix to agree. Use the word in a sentence.

6. _____

_____

At Home: Together, add a suffix to the word *safe.*

Name _____

> You add the suffix -*ive* to a verb to make it a noun. It shows a
> state of being. The vowel in this suffix is short.
>   act + ive = active
> You add the suffix -*age* to a verb to make it a noun. It shows an
> action or a state. You usually drop the silent e.
>   store + age = storage.
> You add the suffix -*ize* to a noun or adjective to make it a verb.
>   civil + ize = civilize.

**A. Read the sentences below. Underline the words with suffixes
that follow the patterns described above.**

1. The passage through the old ship was very narrow.

2. The scuba divers were like underwater detectives.

3. The diver made sure to sterilize his face mask after each use.

4. Did Pete apologize for eating the last sandwich?

5. Pete spent the afternoon exploring the wreckage of the ship.

**B. Choose three underlined words from above. Write sentences
using these words. Underline the words you used.**

6. _____

_____

7. _____

_____

8. _____

_____

At Home: Together, add the suffix –*ive* to *defense* and
offense, then use each word in a sentence.

Exploring the Titanic
Grade 6/Unit 4

125

Name _____

Each underlined word is a vocabulary word.

- Shawn studied a <u>bewildering</u> list of volunteer opportunities.

- Some required a <u>moderate</u> amount of time; others required many hours per week.

- Shawn's broken bike would <u>hamper</u> his transportation and limit his choices.

- He knew that some volunteer organizations <u>prohibit</u> teenagers from volunteering.

- The community center, however, was easily <u>accessible</u> from Shawn's house.

A. Write the definition of each vocabulary word on the line provided.

1. bewildering _____

2. moderate _____

3. hamper _____

4. prohibit _____

5. accessible _____

B. Choose three vocabulary words. Write sentences using these words.

6. _____

_____

7. _____

_____

8. _____

_____

Name _____

When you **compare** and **contrast**, you examine the ways people or things are alike and the ways they are different.

Read the passage below. Then use the checklist to identify the similarities and differences between Aaron and Karen. For each activity, write an X under the name of the character who enjoys it. If both characters enjoy an activity, write an X under both names.

Aaron and Karen are twins. They enjoy many of the same things. For example, they both enjoy playing soccer and watching sports on TV. But when it comes to how they spend their volunteering time, Aaron and Karen are very different.

Karen likes being outdoors. She volunteers at the community center, where she coaches third-graders in soccer, takes them on picnics and hikes, and supervises as they clean up the pond behind the middle school.

Aaron likes technology. He volunteers at the senior center, teaching senior citizens how to use a computer, send e-mail, and use a digital camera. Karen knows how to use a computer as well, but she would rather be outdoors!

Activity	Aaron	Karen
1. playing soccer		
2. watching sports on TV		
3. being outdoors		
4. coaching soccer		
5. picnics and hikes		
6. computers		

© Macmillan/McGraw-Hill

At Home: Together, think of different ways to volunteer in your community. Compare and contrast them.

As you read *Saving Grace*, fill in the Venn Diagram.

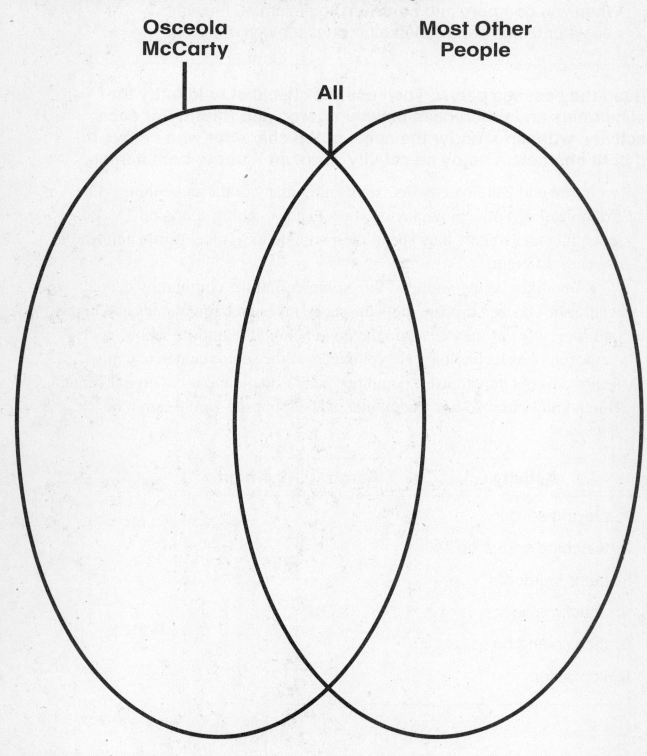

Osceola
McCarty

Most Other
People

All

How does the information you wrote in this Venn Diagram help you
monitor comprehension of *Saving Grace*?

 At Home: Have the student use the chart to retell the story.

As I read, I will pay attention to tempo or expression.

	Americans love rags-to-riches stories. We admire people
7	who start out with little, work hard, and achieve success. That
18	may be because our country started out that way. Many
28	people from other countries have moved here. To immigrants
37	and their children, America has meant a chance for a better
48	life. It was a chance they didn't think they'd have back home.
60	Amadeo Giannini (ah-mah-DAY-oh jah-NEE-nee)
62	lived the dream. His parents came here from Italy.
71	Even as a child, he worked hard in the family business. He
83	learned to judge people quickly. He didn't care how much
93	money they had. What he cared about was what kind of
104	person they were. He wanted to help people in his
114	community. Through his hard work, vision, and desire to
123	help people, he built his business into what is now one of the
136	world's biggest banks. He built the Bank of America. 145

Comprehension Check

1. Why did immigrants move to the United States? What kind of life did they think they had left behind? **Compare and Contrast**

2. What made Giannini a good judge of people? **Make Inferences**

	Words Read	–	Number of Errors	=	Words Correct Score
First Read		–		=	
Second Read		–		=	

At Home: Help the student read the passage, paying attention to the goal at the top of the page.

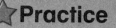
The **parts of a book** can be used to access information about the book as well as its contents.

Title page: This is the first page in the book. It tells the title, the author, and the publisher.

Copyright page: This page tells where and when the book was published and who holds the copyright.

Table of contents: The table of contents lists the titles of units, chapters, or other sections of the book and their page numbers.

Glossary: This part of the book lists and defines any difficult or special terms used in the text.

Index: This is an alphabetical list of all the things mentioned in the book. Each entry has a page number where information on the subject can be found.

Answer the following questions about the parts of a book.

1. Where would you look to find when the book was published?

   _____

2. Where would you look to find the meaning of an unfamiliar word?

   _____

3. You need to know if the book has information on helping endangered animals. Where would you look?

   _____

4. Where would you look to find the author's name?

   _____

5. Where would you look to find the page number for Chapter 2?

   _____

6. Which two parts of a book will give you information about page numbers?

   _____

© Macmillan/McGraw-Hill

 At Home: Together, study the copyright page, table of contents, and index of a cookbook.

Name _____

> **Homographs** are words that are spelled the same but have different definitions and sometimes different pronunciations. For example, *wind* (rhymes with *find*) means to wrap around. *Wind* (rhymes with *pinned*) however, is moving air. Sometimes the words emphasize different syllables. For example, *object* has an emphasis on the first syllable when it means a thing. It has an emphasis on the second syllable when it means to oppose, as in "Your honor, I object!"

Write a definition for each homograph below. Then write a sentence using the homograph. Use a dictionary if you cannot think of two different meanings.

1. nail: _____

_____

nail: _____

_____

2. just: _____

_____

just: _____

_____

3. mine: _____

_____

mine: _____

_____

4. found: _____

_____

found: _____

_____

At Home: Together, find two different meanings for the homograph *fair*.

Saving Grace • Grade 6/Unit 4

© Macmillan/McGraw-Hill

Name _____

Words can begin with a **prefix** and end with a **suffix**.
Sometimes they have both. If you know the meanings of some
common prefixes and suffixes along with the meanings of the
base words, you can often figure out the meaning of a new
word. Some examples are given below.

**Use the meanings of the prefixes and suffixes in the chart to figure
out the meanings of the words. Then write the meaning of the word
on the line.**

Prefix	Meaning
un-, dis-	not
out-	in a way that is greater
en-	put into or onto or cover with
re-	again or back

Suffix	Meaning
-ful	full of
-ment	concrete result of or state of
-ly	in the manner of
-ness	a state or condition of

1. disgraceful _____

2. agreement _____

3. reappointment _____

4. ungrateful _____

5. outdistance _____

6. enjoyment _____

7. reattachment _____

8. unhappiness _____

9. entangle _____

10. rearrange _____

© Macmillan/McGraw-Hill

 At Home: Ask the student to explain the meaning of the
word *disagreement.*

Name _____

Each underlined vocabulary word is shown in context in the following sentences.

- Ashley was asked to give a <u>demonstration</u> of the new bike, showing its features to prospective buyers.

- The company that manufactured the bike was <u>prominent</u>, or widely known.

- The bike was designed for comfort and pleasure, a <u>luxury</u> ride.

- Ashley was <u>adept</u>, or highly skilled, at sales because she was a racer.

- <u>Spectators</u> often came to see her ride in local cycling races.

- Even when some other rider edged her out, Ashley always found a way to <u>prevail</u> and triumph in the race.

- She used skillful and clever moves, and finally <u>maneuvered</u> her way to the front of the pack.

- There was often a <u>collective</u> cheer from the members of the audience as they watched the young girl win.

Use the context clues in the sentences above to write the definition of each vocabulary word.

1. demonstration _____

2. prominent _____

3. luxury _____

4. adept _____

5. spectators _____

6. prevail _____

7. maneuvered _____

8. collective _____

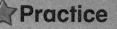

Name _____

A **fact** is information that can be proved. For example, "Boston is the capital of Massachusetts" is a fact. We can use an almanac to prove that Boston exists and that it is the capital of Massachusetts. An **opinion** is a belief that is based on what a person thinks rather than what is proved or known to be true. For example, "Boston has the best team in the American League" is an opinion.

Read the sentences. Circle fact or opinion after each sentence.

1. There are nine planets in our solar system.

   Fact   Opinion

2. Venus is the best planet in our solar system.

   Fact   Opinion

3. There are two kinds of elephants—African elephants and Asian elephants.

   Fact   Opinion

4. There are two kinds of elephants—exciting ones and boring ones.

   Fact   Opinion

5. John Hancock signed his name to the Declaration of Independence in 1776.

   Fact   Opinion

6. John Hancock's graceful signature can still be seen on the Declaration of Independence.

   Fact   Opinion

7. The first Sherlock Holmes tale was *A Study in Scarlet*.

   Fact   Opinion

8. The most popular Sherlock Holmes tale is *The Hound of the Baskervilles*.

   Fact   Opinion

At Home: Together, look for facts and opinions in a magazine or newspaper article.

Name _____

As you read *Major Taylor*, fill in the Fact and Opinion Chart.

Fact	Opinion

How does the information you wrote in this Fact and Opinion Chart help
you monitor comprehension of *Major Taylor*?

At Home: Have the student use the chart to retell the story.

Name _____

As I read, I will pay attention to tempo.

	Tony Hawk was born and raised in southern California.
9	Tony says he was a skinny, hyperactive kid. He was also
20	really hard on himself. From a young age, Tony would
30	accept nothing less than perfection, especially from himself.
38	This worried his parents, so they talked to someone at his
49	school. The school psychologist thought that Tony was
57	gifted. And he was right!
62	It was around this time that the world's future best
72	skater picked up a board for the first time. Tony's brother,
83	Steve, changed his life forever by giving him a skateboard.
93	That first skateboard turned out to be a way for Tony to
105	channel his energy and concentration into something he
113	liked. He practiced on his board every day. His brother Steve
124	remembered how Tony changed as he got better on his
134	board. He noticed that Tony started to calm down. 143

Comprehension Check

1. What opinion did Tony have of himself as a child? **Fact and Opinion**

2. How did the skateboard help Tony become less hyperactive? **Make Inferences**

	Words Read	−	Number of Errors	=	Words Correct Score
First Read		−		=	
Second Read		−		=	

 At Home: Help the student read the passage, paying attention to the goal at the top of the page.

Name _____

Poetry uses words in special ways.
Assonance is the repetition of the same middle vowel sound in
two or more closely grouped words. Examples: *frumpy muppets*,
or *dancing ants*.
Onomatopoeia is a word that sounds like or imitates what it
describes. Examples: *whoosh*, *slurp* or *buzz*.

Read the following poem. Then answer the questions.

Flying fish like to pool,
in Splish-Splash School,
They attend class in how to pass,
on baited hooks or find hiding nooks,
to dart and outsmart pesky predators,
or glide, slide, swoop over hungry carnivores,
They learn fast or find their time is whoosh! past,
It's a zig-zag fish-eat-fish sea,
Or else you're fresh sushi!

A. Write the pairs of words that have assonance.

1. _____   5. _____

2. _____   6. _____

3. _____   7. _____

4. _____   8. _____

B. Answer the following questions.

9. Which words show onomatopoeia? _____

_____

10. What are some words that you could add to the poem that would show

onomatopoeia? _____

At Home: Together, discuss examples of assonance and
onomatopoeia found in comic books.

Major Taylor • Grade 6/Unit 4   137

Using analogies requires you to identify the **relationships** between words. Sometimes the relationship can be synonyms or antonyms. Other times analogies show different relationships. What is the relation between these two words? Sparrow : bird. A sparrow is a kind of bird. Look at the complete analogy and notice how the second set of words shows the same relationship. Sparrow : bird :: poodle : dog. A sparrow is a kind of bird, and a poodle is a kind of dog. The chart below shows other kinds of relationships often tested in analogies.

ANALOGY	EXAMPLE
item : category	chair : furniture
item : purpose	ruler : measure
worker : tool	writer : pencil
worker : product	baker : bread
part : whole	finger : hand

Study the relationship between the first two words. Then circle the letter of the word that shows the same relationship and best completes the analogy.

1. Add : subtract :: come :

   a. sum   **b.** go   **c.** travel   **d.** divide

2. Hour : day :: second :

   a. week   **b.** clock   **c.** time   **d.** minute

3. Apple : fruit :: broccoli :

   a. green   **b.** sour   **c.** vegetable   **d.** dinner

4. Oven : cook :: pencil :

   a. hot   **b.** write   **c.** pen   **d.** paper

5. Tighten : loosen :: empty :

   a. build   **b.** end   **c.** fill   **d.** nail

At Home: Together, decide what type of relationship is shown in this analogy: *Refrigerator is to food as wallet is to money.*

© Macmillan/McGraw-Hill

Name _____

> Sometimes the vowel sounds of base words change with the addition of suffixes. A long sound might become a short sound. For example, *crime* has a long /i/ sound, but *criminal* has a short /i/ sound.

Read the words. Explain how the vowel sound has changed with the addition of a suffix.

1. televise   television   _____

   _____

2. combine   combination   _____

   _____

3. introduce   introduction   _____

   _____

4. please   pleasure   _____

   _____

5. automate   automatic _____

   _____

6. prefer   preferable_____

   _____

At Home: Have the student tell how the vowel sound changes when the suffix is added for *divide/division*.

Major Taylor • Grade 6/Unit 4

139

Name _____

| symmetry | arid | benefit | deftly |
| eaves | furrowed | derision | ceramics |

Use the clues and the vocabulary words to complete the crossword.

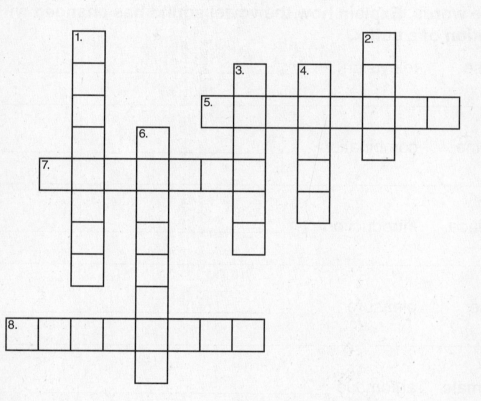

Down

1. balance

2. dry

3. skillfully

4. part of a roof that hangs over the wall

6. the use of ridicule to show contempt

Across

5. articles made by firing clay at a high temperature

7. advantage

8. wrinkled

© Macmillan/McGraw-Hill

An author's purpose for writing is usually to entertain, to persuade, or to inform. An **author's perspective** is how she or he feels toward the subject matter.

Read the newspaper article. Then answer the questions.

Dayton—This week a new place for teens to hang out opened up on Center Avenue. It's not a place to hit tennis balls from a machine or slam hardballs into a net. It is a place where young people can learn the ancient art of ceramics.

Spin the Wheel owner, Joseph Piazza, teaches his young patrons to mold, fire, and paint their own ceramic creations. Creating pottery is truly an art, not merely a craft, and Mr. Piazza is there to guide you through every step of creation. Budding artists, ages twelve through twenty, are encouraged to visit the shop at 1234 Center Avenue and sign up for a hobby that will flex your creative muscles and not simply your biceps.

1. What is the author's purpose for writing this article? _____

_____

_____

2. What is the name of the shop? _____

3. What do you learn about it? _____

_____

4. What is the author's perspective? _____

_____

_____

5. What clues led you to this conclusion? _____

_____

_____

_____

 At Home: Together, read a movie review and discuss the author's perspective.

A Single Shard • **Grade 6/Unit 4**   141

Name _____

As you read *A Single Shard*, fill in the Character Web.

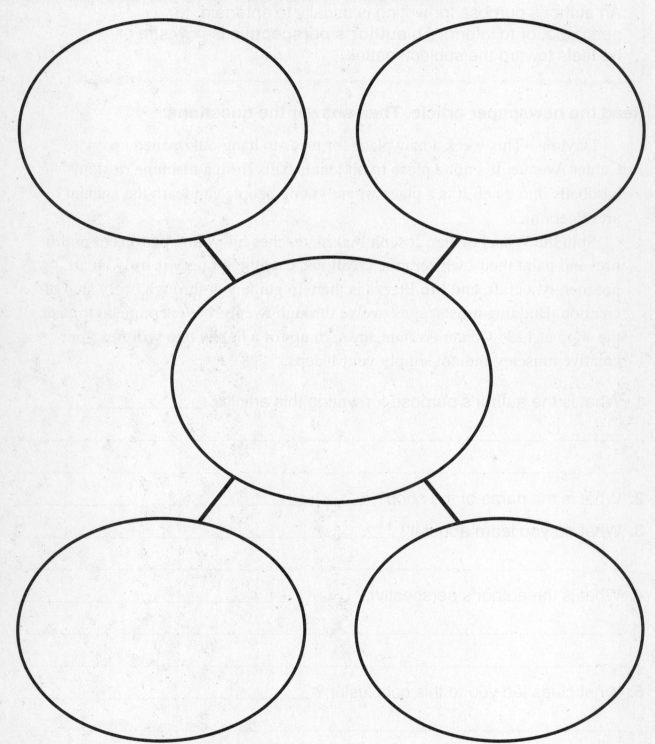

How does the information you wrote in the Author's Perspective Web
help you monitor comprehension of *A Single Shard*?

At Home: Have the student use the chart to retell the story.

Name _____

As I read, I will pay attention to pauses and intonation.

	If you were to travel back in time to Japan in the Middle
13	Ages, you might witness fierce battles between warriors and
22	cruel and bloody wars. But you might also see an artist
33	creating a beautiful piece of pottery or a craftsman making
43	an elaborate sword.
46	Japan was organized by a system called feudalism. At the
56	top of society was the emperor. He was important but didn't
67	control the country. The real ruler was a military leader
77	called a shogun.
80	Below the shogun were powerful landowning lords. Their
88	extended families were called clans. To protect their land,
97	lords needed an army of highly trained warriors. These
106	warriors were called samurai.
110	There were also craftspeople who made swords for the
119	samurai that were works of art and artists created paintings
129	and pottery. Some of the feudal arts and crafts traditions can
140	still be seen in Japanese art today. 147

Comprehension Check

1. Find at least three words in the passage that have homophones. List the words with their homophones. **Homophones**

2. Why does the author want you to know about Japan? **Author's Purpose**

	Words Read	−	Number of Errors	=	Words Correct Score
First Read		−		=	
Second Read		−		=	

 At Home: Help the student read the passage, paying attention to the goal at the top of the page.

Encyclopedias and other reference books use different **typefaces** and sizes to highlight important parts of the text. The title of the entry is bold and in a larger size than the rest of the text.
Words that are important are in bold or in a color that sets them off from the text.
Other topics that relate to the entry, called cross-references, are all in capitals.
Below is an encyclopedia entry about Korean pottery.

Korean Pottery

The Chinese influenced the style, form, glazing methods, and brush techniques of **Korean pottery** for centuries. Korean merchants and traders to China probably brought back the first examples of Chinese pottery and clay. Koreans may have even traveled to China to learn the art of making pottery. During the **Three Kingdoms** period, 57 B.C. to 668 A.D., Korean potters produced plain pottery for ordinary people and very elaborate statues as burial artifacts. The methods used to make these ceramic funeral objects included the ancient methods of **coiling** and **hammering clay**, as well as **potter's wheels**. Scholars have compared the Korean Three Kingdoms pottery to the HAN DYNASTY pottery of CHINA.

Use the encyclopedia entry above to answer the questions.

1. Why is the size of the font for the title of the entry larger than the rest of the text? _____

_____

2. Which kind of typeface is used for the name of the period that this entry talks about? _____

_____

_____

© Macmillan/McGraw-Hill

At Home: Together, find newspaper or magazine articles that have different typefaces and discuss the reasons for the differences.

Homophones are words that sound the same but have different spellings and meanings.
Study the use of the three homophones in this sentence: <u>They're</u> going to get <u>their</u> new ceramics over <u>there</u>. *They're, their,* and *there* are homophones. If you are confused about the meaning or spelling of a homophone, check the dictionary.

Read each sentence. Underline the correct homophones to complete the sentences.

1. (Where, Wear) can I (where, wear) my new red dress?

2. (You're, Your) going to have to get (you're, your) own books.

3. (Two, To, Too) students are going (two, to, too) attend the play (two, too, to).

4. Can you (hear, here) the music from over (here, hear)?

5. (It's, Its) too bad you can't buy (its, it's) matching sweater.

6. Josh had to (pare, pear) forty (pares, pears) to make four pies.

7. Abigail went for a ride on her (horse, hoarse) on a windy day and came back with a (horse, hoarse) voice.

8. Zach had to (pore, pour]) the liquid in the tiny holes or (pores, pours) to do the experiment correctly.

9. Paige was allergic to the (hair's, hare's) long, silky fur or (hair, hare) and sneezed all evening.

10. Bailey paid her bus (fair, fare) to the plaza to attend the book (fair, fare).

At Home: Have the student use the following homophones in a sentence: *there, their, they're.*

Name _____

Sometimes the end consonant sound of a base word changes when you add a suffix.
Study the following rules:
- Words that end with a hard *c* often change to the soft *c* sound with the addition of particular suffixes. For example, the hard *c* of music turns to a soft *c* in *musician*. However, it stays hard in *musical*.
- Words that end in a soft *c* often change to make the /sh/ sound with the addition of the *–ial* suffix. For example, the soft *c* in office changes to /sh/ in *official*.
- When you add the suffix *-ion* to a word, the t-sound changes to a /sh/ sound. For example, the /t/ in select changes to /sh/ in *selection*.

Read the words. Explain how the final consonant sound has changed with the addition of a suffix.

1. face   facial   _____

_____

2. construct   construction   _____

_____

3. critic   criticized   _____

_____

4. attract   attraction   _____

_____

5. medic   medicine   _____

_____

© Macmillan/McGraw-Hill

 At Home: Have the student use the words *construct* and *construction* in a sentence.

Name _____

A. Choose a vocabulary word from the box to answer each question. Write your answer on the line provided.

| adept | guidance | typical | bewildering | accessible |

1. What is another word for help? _____

2. What is another way to say ordinary? _____

3. What is another way to say easy to get to? _____

4. What is a word that means confusing? _____

5. What word means highly skilled? _____

B. Use the correct vocabulary words from the box to fill in the blanks below.

| derision | deftly | benefit | prevail | prominent |

6. Ashley knew she would _____ and win the race.

7. The clown laughed at the bull in _____ but stopped laughing when the bull charged him.

8. Pedro carefully and _____ added a new wireless card to the laptop.

9. Being a few months older than his classmates meant Nate had the

   _____ of getting his driver's license first.

10. The design on the pot had a _____ figure of the sun.

Name _____

A. Choose a vocabulary word from the box to solve each analogy.

| summit | furrowed | interior | prohibit | arid |

1. arctic : cold :: desert : _____

2. basin : valley :: peak : _____

3. flat : smooth :: creased : _____

4. outside : inside :: exterior : _____

5. allow : forbid :: permit : _____

B. Circle the clue that gives a definition of the underlined word.

| wreckage | intact | severed | moderate | maneuvered |

6. Ryan <u>maneuvered</u> his bike to the edge of the pack and skillfully moved past other riders.

7. The children's behavior was surprisingly <u>moderate</u> and even considerate, not extreme.

8. The pile of <u>severed</u> wool grew as the sheepherder cut through the sheep's fleece.

9. A tiny bit of fluff remained <u>intact</u> and in place.

10. After the fire, the ruined ancient city was abandoned and left as <u>wreckage</u>.

Name _____

A. Each underlined vocabulary word is shown in context below. Circle the context clue of the underlined word.

1. William's fine <u>reputation</u>, the way he was seen by others, was well known in his small California town.

2. No one had ever <u>uttered</u> or said a word against Matthew.

3. The <u>migrants</u>, workers who moved from place to place, came to harvest the crops.

4. Jordan knew many of the migrants were working <u>illegally</u>; they were not lawfully employed.

5. No worker was <u>mistreated</u> on Seth's crew; he would not allow his workers to be treated badly.

6. One day, Erika's appendix <u>ruptured</u>, or burst, on the job.

7. Jorge showed his anger that day; his <u>wrath</u> was obvious.

8. Jenna <u>quickened</u> and increased her pace as she ran to the car.

B. Write the definition of each vocabulary word on the line below.

9. reputation _____

10. uttered _____

11. migrant _____

12. illegally _____

13. mistreated _____

14. ruptured _____

15. wrath _____

16. quickened _____

© Macmillan/McGraw-Hill

> An **author's purpose** for writing is usually to entertain, to persuade, or to inform.

Read each situation. Then write the author's main purpose on the line provided: to entertain, to persuade, or to inform.

1. Alicia writes a novel about her experience as a migrant worker.

   _____

2. Monica writes a letter to the governor pleading for funding to start a school for migrant children.

   _____

3. Edward makes a poster telling workers about a night-school opportunity.

   _____

4. Bailey writes a booklet in Spanish telling how to operate the farm's harvesting machine.

   _____

5. Cassandra gives a speech asking members of the community to mentor migrant schoolchildren.

   _____

6. Amy writes a speech explaining why she should be president.

   _____

7. Daniel writes directions on how to set up an e-mail account.

   _____

8. Sasha speaks on the radio asking people to adopt dogs.

   _____

 At Home: Together, read an article from a newspaper and discuss the author's main purpose.

Name _____

As you read *Breaking Through*, fill in the Author's Purpose Chart.

Clues	Author's Purpose

How does the information you wrote in this Author's Purpose Chart help you monitor comprehension of *Breaking Through*?

 At Home: Have the student use the chart to retell the story.

© Macmillan/McGraw-Hill

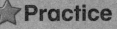
Name _____

As I read, I will pay attention to pauses, stops and intonation.

	Marisol's dad wanted to make a better life for his family and thought
13	that they could do it in the United States. Marisol's dad moved
25	first and when he had enough money, he brought the rest of the family to
40	the United States.
43	Since their arrival in the United States, Rafi was always sad and
55	begged his parents to let him stay home from school. He was sad because
69	he felt like he didn't have many friends. Marisol's parents tried to make
82	him feel better by telling him that it was hard now, but that later he
97	would have a lot of friends. Marisol noticed that her little brother really
110	didn't understand what his parents meant and felt bad for him. Marisol also
123	felt sad until she met Amelia. Amelia really knew how to cheer Marisol up
137	when she felt lonely.
141	But then last week, Marisol noticed a change in Rafi. She didn't know
154	what to think of it. She had noticed that Rafi had started to get up early and
171	walk to school very fast in the mornings. Every time Marisol would try to
185	catch up with Rafi, he would just quicken his pace. 195

Comprehension Check

1. Why do you think Rafi is uncomfortable in school? **Draw Conclusions**

2. Why do you think the author wrote about the experience of being lonely in a new town? **Author's Perspective**

	Words Read	–	Number of Errors	=	Words Correct Score
First Read		–		=	
Second Read		–		=	

 At Home: Help the student read the passage, paying attention to the goal at the top of the page

Name _____

A **schedule** lists times, places, or events in a table. An airline schedule, like the one shown, lists the places and times airplanes arrive and depart. It also lists their flight numbers. Read a schedule just as you would read a table: Read down each column and across each row. Every airline terminal is represented by a series of initials, called the airport code. Notice that the codes do not always conform to the airport's name.

Orlando International Airport, Orlando, FL   MCO
Chicago-O'Hare International Airport, Chicago, IL   ORD
John F. Kennedy International Airport, New York, NY JFK
Houston Intercontinental Airport, Houston, TX   IAH
Los Angeles International Airport, Los Angeles, CA   LAX

Mr. Gillespie has been asked to speak at a conference on mentoring in Houston, Texas. He must fly from Los Angeles to Houston. Use the airline schedule to answer the questions.

FLIGHTS FROM LOS ANGELES (LAX) TO HOUSTON (IAH)

FLIGHT #	DEPARTS LAX	ARRIVES IAH
1794	9:20 A.M.	10:56 A.M.
622	2:25 P.M.	3:59 A.M.
1095	5:50 P.M.	7:29 P.M.
1495	6:50 P.M.	8:34 P.M.

1. What time does Flight 1095 arrive in Houston? _____

2. What time does Flight 622 leave Los Angeles? _____

3. What is the number of the last flight to leave Los Angeles? _____

4. Which flight will get Mr. Gillespie to Houston in time to make a speech at noon? _____

5. Circle the information that is not on the schedule.

flight number   departure time   fare (cost of flight)

At Home: Ask the student to choose the earliest flight he or she could take to Houston from Los Angeles if school gets out at 3 P.M.

If you know the meanings of base words and roots, you can often find the meaning of new words. **Word families** are groups of related words. You can build word families by thinking of the different parts of speech that a root or a base word can make.

A word family for *succeed: success, successful, successfully, unsuccessful, unsuccessfully*

Use the chart to build a word family for each of the words listed. List as many related words as you can—at least three for each word. Use a dictionary if necessary.

stop	lock	pass

comfort	load	migrant

At Home: Have the student build a word family for the word *treat*.

© Macmillan/McGraw-Hill

Words that sound alike but are spelled differently are called **homophones**. These words are reminders that different letters and their combinations can stand for the same sound.

For example, the homophone of *threw* is spelled *through.* It helps to memorize some of these words.

A. Give the homophones for each pair of clues. Make sure you spell the different words correctly. Use a dictionary if necessary.

1. something you write a letter on / something that stays still

   _____

2. the price of a train or plane ticket / a place with rides and games

   _____

3. plant something / use a needle and thread

   _____

4. the opposite of old / had an understanding of

   _____

5. the act of selling something at a bargain price / catches the wind on a boat

   _____

6. something you say to a pest / a covering for a foot

   _____

B. Use the space below to draw a picture for one set of homophones.

At Home: Have the student use the homophones
tale/tail in sentences.

Breaking Through • **Grade 6/Unit 5**   155

Name _____

| encounter | victorious | grimaced | participate |
| ordeals | nourishing | anticipated | dejectedly |

A. Read the passage below. Each underlined word is a vocabulary word.

Stan looked forward to his <u>encounter</u> with the rival debate team. Stan wanted to be sure his team was <u>victorious</u> this time. He <u>grimaced,</u> remembering their last encounter with this school's team. Stan made sure his best debaters were available to <u>participate</u> in this debate. Jennifer and Sue had been through many debating <u>ordeals.</u> The two girls always ate a <u>nourishing</u> meal before the trip to another school. They trained together and <u>anticipated</u> any fact or idea that might come up. In the end no one was going to be thinking <u>dejectedly</u> about what went wrong.

B. Write the letter of the definition beside each vocabulary word in column 1.

1. encounter ____
2. victorious ____
3. grimaced ____
4. participate ____
5. ordeals ____
6. nourishing ____
7. anticipated ____
8. dejectedly ____

a. severe trials or experiences
b. expected
c. having won
d. with sadness
e. take part
f. made a facial expression of disgust
g. nutritious
h. a meeting

© Macmillan/McGraw-Hill

Name _____

> When you **compare and contrast**, you examine the ways that two or more people or things are alike and the ways that they are different.

A. Read the paragraph below. Then use the checklist to identify the similarities and differences between Jennifer and Sue. For each activity, write an X under the name of the character who enjoys it. If both characters enjoy an activity, write an X under both names.

Jennifer and Sue live in the same apartment building on the same floor. They go to the same school and are in the same grade. But that is about all that the girls had in common. Jennifer is an athlete, captain of the field hockey team, and lead racer on the swimming team. She pitches on the softball team and is goalie on the soccer team.

Sue excels in chess, writing, and music. She plays the bass in the orchestra. Sue can fix any computer bug around. Sue recently talked Jennifer into joining the debate team. Now Jennifer and Sue have one more thing in common. They are both champion debaters!

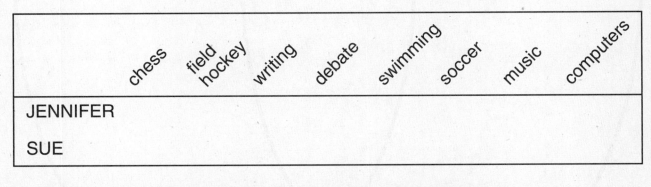

	chess	field hockey	writing	debate	swimming	soccer	music	computers
JENNIFER								
SUE								

B. Write a sentence or two that compares and contrasts the two girls.

_____

_____

_____

_____

 At Home: Have the student name two activities you have in common and two you do not.

Name _____

As you read *Ta-Na-E-Ka*, fill in the Venn Diagram.

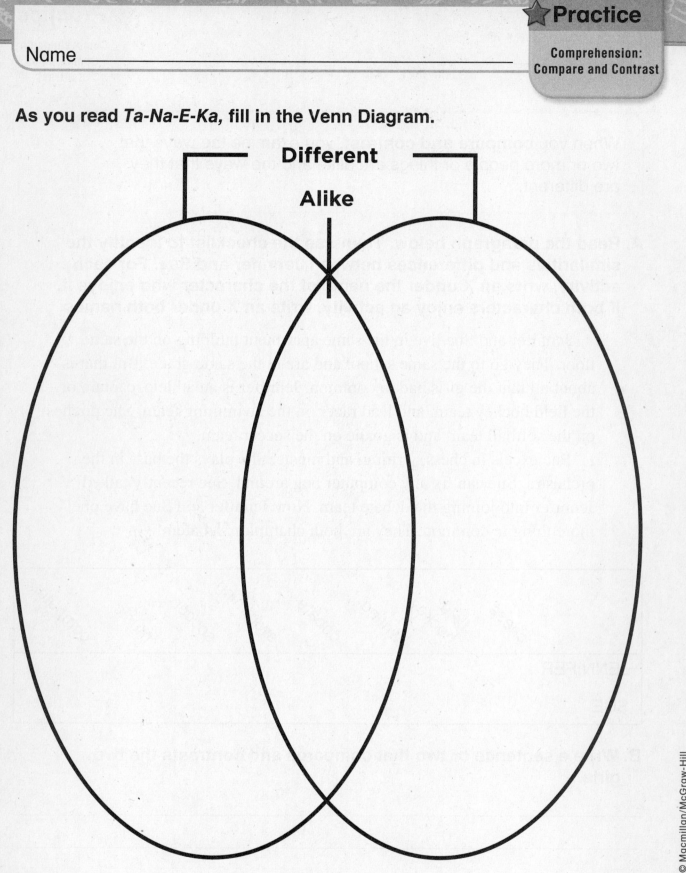

Different

Alike

How does the information you wrote in this Venn Diagram help you
monitor comprehension of *Ta-Na-E-Ka*?

© Macmillan/McGraw-Hill

 At Home: Have the student use the chart to retell the story.

Name _____

As I read, I will pay attention to punctuation and characters' voices.

	Zach was laughing so hard he could barely keep the camera steady.
12	When Manuel launched into his Britney Spears imitation, Zach lost all
23	control. His best friend's face wobbled in the viewfinder and then
34	completely disappeared as Zach sank to the floor, clutching his stomach,
45	and gasped, "Cut!"
48	Annoyed, Manuel **grimaced** at the interruption. He waited until Zach's
58	laughter died down. Then he said, "Come on, man, this is serious."
70	"How can it be serious?" Zach said, starting to laugh again. "You're
82	doing a comedy routine."
86	"Listen—I want to win the audition for the television show, and that's
99	no joke."
101	For once, Zach knew his friend wasn't kidding. The two boys had
113	been watching television together yesterday when the announcement
121	about the talent search came on. It was a nationwide competition. To
133	enter, you had to send in a videotape of yourself performing. One
145	hundred finalists would win tickets to New York—and the chance to
157	audition for a starring role in a new comedy show. 167

Comprehension Check

1. What can you tell about Manuel's character from the passage above? **Character**

2. How does the author use humor in the story? **Author's Purpose**

	Words Read	−	Number of Errors	=	Words Correct Score
First Read		−		=	
Second Read		−		=	

At Home: Help the student read the passage, paying attention to the goal at the top of the page

Ta-Na-E-Ka • Grade 6/Unit 5

159

© Macmillan/McGraw-Hill

A fable is a short story that teaches a moral, often through the actions of animals that act like people.

A **moral** is a lesson taught by a fable or story. It is usually stated outright at the end of the fable.

Personification is a literary device where human characteristics are given to animals or things.

Read the fable. Then answer the questions.

The Lioness

All the mother animals of the forest were boasting one day about who could have the most babies at one time.

"I can have many, many babies at once," said the mother wolf proudly. "I am surely the winner of this contest!"

None of the other mother animals answered, for not one of them could make this boast.

Wolf looked around proudly. Then she noticed the lioness, who sat quietly at the back of the clearing. "And to how many cubs do you give birth?" asked Wolf.

"Only one," answered the lioness quietly, "but that one is a lion!"

Moral: *"Quality is more important than quantity."*

1. What makes this story a fable? _____

_____

2. Who are the main characters in the fable? _____

3. How is the wolf like a person? _____

4. What is the moral of the story? _____

_____

At Home: Together, discuss how the animal characters in a fable act like people.

Name _____

> Many English words have **Latin roots**. Knowing Latin root meanings will help you determine the meanings of English words. The roots cannot always stand alone as words.
>
> The Latin root *ject* means "to throw." In the word *dejectedly*, the root means "put down" or "thrown down." Dejectedly means "cast down in spirits."

A. Make as many words as possible with the Latin roots below. Use a dictionary if necessary.

1. Latin root *vita*, which means "life" _____

_____

2. Latin root *struct*, which means "to build" _____

_____

_____

3. Latin root *spect*, which means "to view" _____

_____

4. Latin root *port*, which means "to carry" _____

_____

5. Latin root *ject*, which means "to throw" _____

_____

B. Use at least one of the words you wrote above in a sentence of your own.

6. _____

_____

At Home: Have the student make as many words as possible from the Latin root *grat*, which means "thankful".

Ta-Na-E-Ka • **Grade 6/Unit 5**   161

Name _____

Many words in English have roots in Latin. When you know the
meaning of **Latin roots**, you can often figure out the meaning of
a new word. Roots do not normally stand alone as words.

**A. Underline the Latin root of each word. Then write the meaning of
the word on the line provided. Use a dictionary if you need to.**

1. important _____

2. contract _____

3. imported _____

4. script _____

5. spectator _____

6. disrespected _____

7. retract _____

8. scribbling _____

B. Add prefixes and suffixes to make new words.

9. Add the prefix *trans–* and the suffix *–ation* to the Latin root *port*. Write the
   word on the line. _____

10. Add the prefix *im–* and the suffix *–ant* to the Latin root *port*. Write the
    word on the line. _____

© Macmillan/McGraw-Hill

162 Ta-Na-E-Ka • **Grade 6/Unit 5**

At Home: Help the student identify the meaning of the
word *vitality*.

Name _____

A. Each underlined vocabulary word is shown in context below. Circle the context clue of the underlined word.

1. Kaylen's mother worked with <u>economists</u>, people who study the economy.

2. She studied the <u>continuous</u> and uninterrupted rise in the price of goods and services over in time.

3. The <u>chronology</u>, or arrangement in order of occurrence, of the e-mails told a story about two pen pals.

4. Susan knew that there was a new video game about to <u>debut</u>, or make a first appearance.

5. A rise in prices is <u>periodic</u> in our country's history, occurring at regular intervals.

B. Write the definition of each vocabulary word on the line provided. Use the context clues above if needed.

6. economists _____

7. continuous _____

8. chronology _____

9. debut _____

10. periodic _____

C. Choose two vocabulary words and write sentences for them.

11. _____

    _____

12. _____

    _____

When writers want to convince others to think in a certain way about a subject, they use a technique called **persuasion**. A piece of persuasive writing usually has a main point or opinion supported by logically presented details. It often uses strong language or persuasive words such as *should* or *must*.

Read the following poster. Then answer the questions below.

> **The Rivington Community Recycling Center is now open!**
> Hours: Monday through Saturday, 10 a.m. to 5 p.m.
> - Everyone in our community should use the recycling center.
> - People should bring in their paper products once a week.
> - Bring any glass and plastic bottles to the center every two weeks.
> - Remember, when we recycle we not only protect our environment, but we also help restore our town!

1. What is one example of persuasive writing in the poster?

_____

_____

2. What is a second example of persuasive writing in the poster?

_____

_____

3. What is the central message of the fourth point on the poster?

_____

_____

4. Sum up the purpose of the poster.

_____

_____

 At Home: Together, make up a poster to encourage people in the neighborhood not to litter.

Name _____

As you read *Many Countries, One Currency*, fill in the
Persuasion Chart.

Word or phrase	Kind of persuasion

How does the information you wrote in this Persuasion Chart help you
monitor comprehension of *Many Countries, One Currency*?

 At Home: Have the student use the chart to retell the story.

Many Countries, One Currency
Grade 6/Unit 5

Name _____

As I read, I will pay attention to pronunciation of vocabulary and other difficult words.

	Alexander Hamilton's portrait is on the $10 bill. But he was never
11	president of the United States. Who was he? He was one of the most
25	important Founding Fathers. The Founding Fathers were the group of
35	leaders who helped found the United States.
42	Hamilton was a young military officer during the American
51	Revolution. He spent most of the war serving as General George
62	Washington's aide. After the war, he became one of the leaders who
74	helped create the Constitution.
78	Washington appointed Hamilton as the nation's first Secretary of the
88	Treasury. He was one of the country's first **economists**. He helped
99	organize the nation's finances. Many Americans thought that Congress
108	should be more powerful than the president. Hamilton argued that the
119	president needed to be at least as strong as Congress.
129	Two presidents and a Founding Father are on the $20, $50, and $100
139	bills. Andrew Jackson is shown on the $20 bill. He was a military hero
152	and the seventh president of the United States. 160

Comprehension Check

1. Why do you think Hamilton's face is on the $10 bill? **Make Inferences**

2. What opinion did Hamilton have about a president's power? What happened as a result of Hamilton's opinion? **Fact and Opinion**

	Words Read	−	Number of Errors	=	Words Correct Score
First Read		−		=	
Second Read		−		=	

© Macmillan/McGraw-Hill

166 Many Countries, One Currency
Grade 6/Unit 5

At Home: Help the student read the passage, paying attention to the goal at the top of the page

Name _____

A **dictionary** gives the definitions of words. It also shows the pronunciation, the parts of speech, and how to divide the syllables. Look at this entry:

    dol•lar ('dol ́ər) *n.* **1.** the standard unit of money in the United States **2.** a coin, note, or token representing one dollar

A **thesaurus** lists synonyms and antonyms of a word. Look at this entry:

    end
    NOUNS

    1. conclusion   close, finish, completion, finale

    2. purpose   aim, objective, goal, reason, intention

    ANTONYMS: beginning, commencement, start

    VERB

    conclude   settle, close, complete, finish

Use the sample entries to answer the questions.

1. How many definitions are listed for the word *dollar*? _____

2. What part of speech is the word *dollar*? _____

3. What two parts of speech can the word *end* be used as?

_____

4. Name three synonyms for the word *end* as a noun meaning *purpose.*

_____

5. Name the antonyms for the word *end*.

_____

6. If you wanted to find a substitute word for *dollar*, which resource would be

the best choice? _____

At Home: Have the student use a synonym for the word *end* in a sentence.

Name _____

Many English words have **Greek roots**. These roots cannot always stand alone as words. Recognizing Greek root meanings will help you understand the meanings of English words. The Greek root *auto* means "self" or "person." The word *autograph,* means "a person's handwritten signature."

Make as many words as possible with the Greek roots below. Use a dictionary if necessary.

1. Greek root *bio,* which means "life" _____

   _____

2. Greek root *log* or *logi,* which means "reason" or "science"

   _____

3. Greek root *phil,* which means "love" _____

   _____

4. Greek root *gram* or *graph,* which means "to write" _____

   _____

5. Greek root *astr,* which means "star" _____

   _____

6. Greek root tele, which means "far off" _____

   _____

7. Greek root *path,* which means "feeling," "suffering," or "disorder"

   _____

8. Greek root *cycl,* which means "circle," or "wheel"

   _____

168 Many Countries, One Currency
Grade 6/Unit 5

At Home Have the student make some words from the Greek root *mono,* meaning "alone, single."

© Macmillan/McGraw-Hill

Name _____

Some words in English have **Greek roots**. When you know the
Greek roots, you can break words down into their parts. This will
help you find their meanings. Root words can be bases, or they
can be prefixes and/or suffixes.

**A. Circle the root or roots in each word. Write the meaning of at
least one of the roots on the line.**

1. biological _____

_____

2. epigraph _____

_____

3. automobile _____

_____

4. chlorophyll _____

_____

5. biology _____

_____

6. astronomy _____

_____

7. automobile _____

_____

8. telegraph _____

_____

At Home: Have the student identify the meaning of
the word *polysyllabic*.

© Macmillan/McGraw-Hill

Name _____

A. Read the following sentences. Underline the vocabulary word and circle the context clue in each sentence.

dilapidated	decades	rafters	instinctively
swiveled	auction	decrease	shakily

1. Judith picked up the dilapidated old book from the trunk in the attic.

2. It had been published decades ago and was perfect for her book collection.

3. The rafters above her were made of oak.

4. She instinctively looked up without thinking, when she heard a noise.

5. Miranda swiveled on her rotating seat.

6. The auction for the sale of the antique books was about to begin.

7. Would the price she had been quoted increase or decrease?

8. The very old woman, who also wanted the book, walked down the aisle shakily.

B. Write the letter of the definition beside each vocabulary word in the first column.

9. dilapidated _____   a. the opposite of increase

10. decades _____   b. characterized by shaking

11. rafters _____   c. naturally, without thinking

12. instinctively _____   d. a sale of property to the highest bidder

13. swiveled _____   e. decayed through neglect or misuse

14. auction _____   f. parallel beams that support a roof

15. decrease _____   g. periods of ten years

16. shakily _____   h. swung or rotated

Name _____

> When you decide what you think or feel about a character's actions or about story events, you make a **judgment**. To make a judgment, you should consider the reasons for and against a decision by using the story information and your own experience.

1. Molly lends India a book that Molly really likes. India does not enjoy the book. When Molly asks India her opinion of the book, what should India tell Molly?

   _____

   _____

   _____

2. At a store a salesperson rings up the wrong price at the cash register. What should Andy do?

   _____

   _____

3. Josh's mom asks him to skip soccer practice, which he really enjoys. What should Josh tell his mom?

   _____

   _____

4. Someone steps to the front of a line by accident. What should Sarah do?

   _____

   _____

5. Michael finds a wallet on the street that has pictures, but no other identification. What should Michael do?

   _____

   _____

 At Home: Together, discuss a situation where you have to make a judgment.

© Macmillan/McGraw-Hill

Name _____

As you read *Honus and Me,* fill in the Make Judgments Chart.

Action	Judgment

How does the information you wrote in this Make Judgments Chart help you monitor comprehension of *Honus and Me*?

At Home: Have the student use the chart to retell the story.

© Macmillan/McGraw-Hill

Name _____

As I read, I will pay attention to tempo.

	Feel the change in your pocket. You can probably identify
10	each coin instinctively. Dimes are thin and small. Nickels are
20	larger. Their edges are smooth. Quarters are the biggest coin.
30	They are a little thinner than nickels but much thicker than
41	dimes. Quarters also have grooves around the edges.
49	The quarter was first introduced in 1796. What did
57	old quarters look like? For over 100 years, the front of this
68	coin featured a woman. She represented liberty. The design
77	of the quarter was changed in 1932. To celebrate the 200th
86	anniversary of George Washington's birthday, the face of the
93	quarter began to feature our first president.
102	Quarters were changed again in 1999. The 50
108	State Quarters® Program was launched. Fifty new quarters,
116	one for each state, were to be designed and produced. The
127	faces of the new quarters would remind us of the history of
139	America.
140	In 1789 the United States established its first government.
148	The Constitution had just been ratified, or approved, by all
158	13 states. George Washington had been chosen as the first
167	president. 168

Comprehension Check

1. Why do you think coins are made to be identifiable by touch? **Draw Conclusions**

2. Why do you think the author wrote about quarters? **Author's Purpose**

	Words Read	–	Number of Errors	=	Words Correct Score
First Read		–		=	
Second Read		–		=	

At Home: Help the student read the passage, paying attention to the goal at the top of the page

Honus and Me • **Grade 6/Unit 5**

Articles in magazines, newspapers, and textbooks often include photos. Photos enrich an article by showing the reader something words cannot. Often a photo has a caption—a sentence or two beneath or beside the photo. Captions describe what is in the photo, and often give the reader additional information.

Study the drawing of a photograph and the caption below. Use them to answer the questions.

In 1947, Jack Roosevelt (Jackie) Robinson was the first African American man to play in the major leagues. Mr. Robinson led the Brooklyn Dodgers to six National League titles and one victorious World Series. Mr. Robinson was active in the civil rights movement. He is shown in August 1963 with his son, David, being interviewed at the march on Washington.

1. Who is shown in the photograph? _____

_____

2. Why was Jackie Robinson famous? _____

_____

3. How many World Series did Jackie Robinson win? _____

4. Where and when was the photograph taken? _____

_____

5. In what area besides baseball was Jackie Robinson active? _____

_____

At Home: Have the student find a photo in the newspaper with a caption. Discuss the photo and caption.

Name _____

Dictionaries and thesauruses list words of similar meaning
(*synonyms*) and also words of opposite meaning (***antonyms***).

**A. On the lines provided, write an antonym for each word below.
Use a dictionary or thesaurus if you need help.**

WORD	ANTONYM
1. nervous	_____
2. rapidly	_____
3. sturdy	_____
4. specific	_____
5. beneficial	_____
6. incompetent	_____
7. complex	_____
8. soon	_____
9. brave	_____
10. easy	_____

**B. Choose two of the antonyms you wrote and use each one in a
sentence of your own. Underline the antonyms you use in your
sentences.**

11. _____

    _____

12. _____

    _____

© Macmillan/McGraw-Hill

At Home Have the student identify an antonym for the word
serious.

Honus and Me • **Grade 6/Unit 5**   175

Name _____

The suffixes **-able** and **-ible** both mean "able or likely." For example, *respectable* means able or likely to be respected. You decide which spelling you will use based on whether you are attaching the suffix to a base word, such as *respect* (respect**able**) or a word root, such as *vis* (vis**ible**).

Another choice you may have to make is whether or not to drop the *e* of the base word before adding *-able.* Look at these two examples: bridgeable and usable. When the base word ends in a soft /g/ or /c/ sound, it keeps the silent *e* when you add the *-able ending.*

A. Read the sentences below. Add the correct suffix, either -able or -ible.

1. Judy found it imposs_____ to walk by a used book store.

2. Fortunately, her work hours were extremely flex_____.

3. Sometimes she made a remark_____ find for her collection of antique books.

4. She found book collecting a very manage_____ hobby.

5. Judy was never disagree _____ with bookstore owners.

6. She knew that bad manners in business were unaccept_____.

7. She did not treat people as if they were invis_____.

8. Judy's manners in business and in her personal life were

   admir_____.

B. Write two sentences that include words that have the -able or -ible suffixes. Underline the words with the suffixes.

9. _____

10. _____

   _____

 At Home: Have the student use the word *perishable* in a sentence.

© Macmillan/McGraw-Hill

Name _____

A. Circle the context clue for the underlined vocabulary word in each of the following sentences.

1. Jackie Robinson had the courage of his <u>convictions</u>, his strong beliefs.

2. He had experienced <u>oppression</u>—the unjust exercise of authority.

3. It was clear and <u>evident</u> to Jackie that African American men should be able to play in major league baseball.

4. There were few <u>remedies</u>, or legal means to right a wrong, at that time.

5. Jackie Robinson was <u>persistent</u>, never giving up.

6. He was known for his <u>defiance</u>, willingness to fight for what he believed was right.

7. As the years went by, he gained <u>momentum</u>, strength or force gained by motion.

8. When Jackie Robinson joined the Dodgers the victory <u>resonated,</u> or echoed, within the civil rights movement.

B. Write the definition of each vocabulary word on the line provided.

9. convictions _____

10. oppression _____

11. evident _____

12. remedies _____

13. persistent _____

14. defiance _____

15. momentum _____

16. resonated _____

Summarize each paragraph below in one sentence on the line provided. Use your own words.

1. Is there something going on in your community that makes you want to take a stand? One person's voice may not get noticed, but many people joined together cannot be ignored.
   Summary:

   _____

   _____

2. Jackie Robinson was an athlete who wanted to make a change. He was a strong man, willing to fight for his right to play in the major leagues. But he knew that fighting back would not win him the recognition he wanted.
   Summary:

   _____

   _____

3. Jackie Robinson won all kinds of awards in baseball: Rookie of the Year, Most Valuable Player, and he was inducted into the Baseball Hall of Fame. He is most famous for breaking the color barrier in baseball.
   Summary:

   _____

   _____

   _____

4. After retiring from baseball, Robinson became more active in the civil rights movement, sat on the boards of corporations, founded a bank, and established a scholarship fund for minority students.
   Summary:

   _____

   _____

© Macmillan/McGraw-Hill

 At Home Together, read and discuss the life of an activist such as Jackie Robinson.

Name _____

As you read *Let It Shine: Rosa Parks*, fill in the Summary Chart.

Beginning	Middle	End

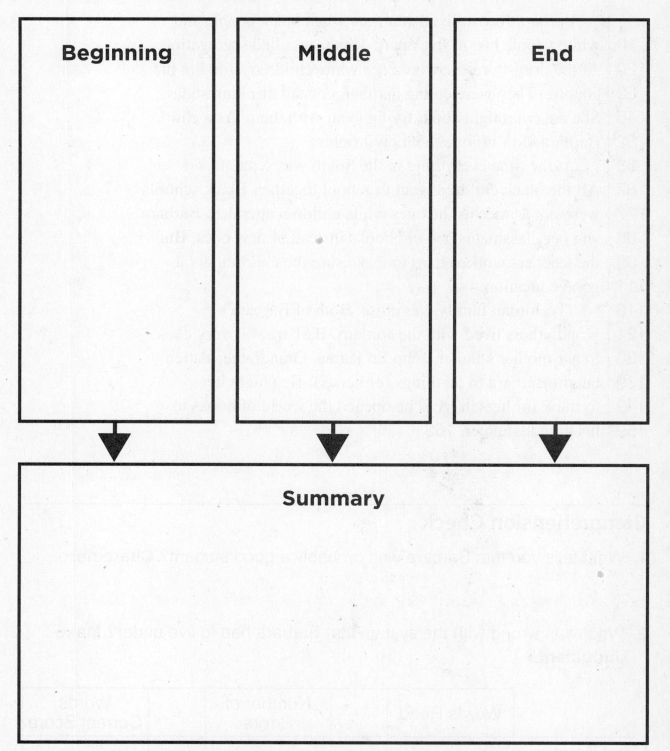

Summary

How does the information you wrote in this Summary Chart help you monitor comprehension of *Let It Shine: Rosa Parks*?

 At Home: Have the student use the chart to retell the story.

As I read, I will pay attention to tempo.

10	Barbara Jordan lived at a time when black people and
20	white people had to live apart. This was called segregation.
32	At the drug store she would see white children sitting at the
40	counter. They were eating hamburgers and drinking sodas.
52	She never thought about trying to sit with them. As a child,
58	Barbara didn't think about civil rights.
67	At the time everything in the South was separate.
77	All the black children went to school together. Black schools
88	were not as nice as the ones white children attended. Barbara
99	and her classmates had old books instead of new ones. But
111	the teachers worked hard to make sure the children got a
113	good education.
121	The Jordan family was close. Both of Barbara's
130	grandfathers lived with the Jordans. Barbara was very close
139	to her mother's father, John Ed Patten. Grandfather Patten
149	taught Barbara to do things for herself. He taught her
159	to think for herself. And he opened the world of books to
	his granddaughter. 163

Comprehension Check

1. What tells you that Barbara was probably a good student? **Character**

2. What was wrong with the system that Barbara had to live under? **Make Judgments**

	Words Read	–	Number of Errors	=	Words Correct Score
First Read		–		=	
Second Read		–		=	

At Home: Help the student read the passage, paying attention to the goal at the top of the page.

> **Rhyme** is the repetition of syllables with the same vowel and consonant sounds.
> Example: Jack and *Jill*
>   Went up the *hill*
>
> **Simile** is a comparison of unlike things, using the words *like* or *as.*
> Example: The pie pastry was as light as a feather.
>
> **Repetition** is the repeating of a word or phrase.
> Example: *Rosy, rosy,* my little posy.

Read the following lines by Henry Wadsworth Longfellow from "Afternoon in February." Then answer the questions.

> The day is ending,
> The night descending;
> The marsh is frozen,
> The river dead.
> Through clouds like ashes
> The red sun flashes
> On village windows
> That glimmer red.

1. Find examples of rhyme.

   _____

2. Find an example of a simile.

   _____

3. What two unlike things are being compared in this simile?

   _____

4. How are the unlike things alike?

   _____

   _____

 At Home Together, read a poem discussing the author's use of rhyme, or other figurative language.

Let It Shine: Rosa Parks
Grade 6/Unit 5

Name _____

You can define an unknown word by using the words surrounding it to give you clues to the word's meaning. Often, a **context clue** will give examples of the word's meaning. Find the context clue in this sentence:

Fossil fuels, such as coal, oil, and natural gas, are nonrenewable sources of energy.

The sentence gives you three examples of *fossil fuels* and tells you what they are.

Circle the context clues to help you figure out the meaning of each underlined word below. Write the meaning on the line provided. Use a dictionary if necessary.

1. The new student's <u>apparel</u> consisted of a pair of blue jeans, sneakers, and a white tuxedo shirt.

_____

2. A child's first words often name <u>tangible</u> objects—those that can be touched or felt, such as a toy.

_____

3. Lions are <u>carnivorous</u> animals. They eat the meat of other animals rather than plant life.

_____

4. The house was unusually quiet and peaceful that day, as <u>tranquil</u> as a meadow on a quiet afternoon.

_____

5. My cat is an <u>obstinate</u> creature—like a stubborn mule that refuses to come just for the sake of refusing.

_____

© Macmillan/McGraw-Hill

At Home Have the student use one of the words above in a sentence.

Name _____

The **suffixes** -*ant*, -*ent*, -*ance*, and -*ence* are closely related except for the way they are spelled.

The suffixes -*ant* and -*ent* mean being or performing what the root means.

The suffixes -*ance* and -*ence* mean the quality of having, showing, or making what the root means.

There is no easy rule for choosing the correct spelling, but if you know the spelling of one form, then you know the spelling of the other form.

Example: important, importance   present, presence

For each word or root below write the correct form of it, using the suffixes above. Use a dictionary to help if you need to.

Root	-*ant* or -*ent*	-*ance* or -*ence*
1. resist	_____	_____
2. differ	_____	_____
3. persist	_____	_____
4. indulge	_____	_____
5. excel	_____	_____
6. radi	_____	_____
7. vigil	_____	_____
8. hesitate	_____	_____

© Macmillan/McGraw-Hill

At Home Have the student use the word *observant* in a sentence.

Name _____

A. Choose a vocabulary word from the box to answer each question. Write your answer on the line provided.

> reputation   mistreated   wrath   victorious   anticipated

1. What is another word for expected? _____

2. What is another way to say treated badly? _____

3. What is another way to refer to your character as seen by others?

_____

4. What is a word that means anger? _____

5. What word means you have won? _____

B. Use the correct vocabulary words from the box to make sense in the sentences below.

> ordeals   encounter   debut   periodic   continuous

6. The singer made her _____ in a musical.

7. The _____ clanging of the school bell gave her a headache.

8. The _____ dripping of the faucet wasted water.

9. The final _____ in the novel was a duel.

10. The hero suffered through many difficult _____.

At Home Have the student use the word *grimaced* in a sentence.

Name _____

A. Circle the context clue of the underlined word.

| remedies | rafters | decrease | evident | defiance |

1. He was surprised by the peasants' <u>defiance</u> and refusal to pay.

2. The drop in attendance caused a <u>decrease</u> in sales.

3. Jenny's note was <u>evident</u> to the teacher, but not obvious to Sam.

4. Willow bark was one of the <u>remedies</u> and cures for a toothache.

5. The holiday lights hung from the <u>rafters</u> and ceiling beams.

B. Write the letter of the correct definition next to each vocabulary word.

| momentum | decades | instinctively | dilapidated | chronology |

6. instinctively ____   **a.** ruined or decayed

7. dilapidated ____   **b.** periods of ten years

8. chronology ____   **c.** relating to a natural tendency

9. momentum ____   **d.** force resulting from motion

10. decades ____   **e.** arrangement of events in sequence

Name _____

A. Circle the context clue of the underlined vocabulary word in each sentence.

1. Abe enjoyed reading about the <u>Renaissance,</u> a flowering of the arts and literature in Europe beginning in the fourteenth century.

2. He studied the works of one <u>philosopher,</u> a person who seeks wisdom.

3. Abe was designing an <u>elaborate</u> painting, marked by complex colors and textures.

4. His neighbor wanted to <u>recommend</u> Abe for a painting job, to endorse him as fit, worthy, and competent.

5. Soon the school board ordered Abe, or <u>commissioned</u> him, to do the job.

6. First Abe made a <u>miniature</u> painting, or a small one just like the large one would be.

7. He pictured to himself, or <u>envisioned,</u> something very colorful and grand.

8. Abe worked hard to make sure that everything was in <u>proportion</u>—the harmonious relation of parts to each other.

B. Write the definition of each vocabulary word on the line provided.

9. Renaissance _____

_____

10. philosopher _____

11. elaborate _____

12. recommend _____

13. commissioned _____

14. miniature _____

15. envisioned _____

16. proportion _____

© Macmillan/McGraw-Hill

A **generalization** is a broad statement based on a number of details. Generalizations often contain words such as *all, always, often, many, most, none, least*. A good generalization cannot be proved false.

Write a generalization to answer each question. Use one of the following words to make each generalization: *all, always, often, many, most, none, least*. Underline the word.

1. What generalization could you make about people who visit art museums frequently?

   _____

   _____

   _____

2. What generalization could you make about someone who can draw, paint, sculpt, and design websites?

   _____

   _____

   _____

3. What generalization could you make about houses that people enjoy living in?

   _____

   _____

   _____

4. What generalization could you make about architects who design such houses?

   _____

   _____

   _____

 At Home Ask the student to answer this question: What generalization could you make about how responsible you are about homework?

Leonardo's Horse • **Grade 6/Unit 6** 187

Name _____

As you read *Leonardo's Horse* fill in the Generalizations Chart.

Important Information	Generalization

How does the information you wrote in this Generalizations Chart help
you monitor comprehension of *Leonardo's Horse*?

At Home: Have the student use the chart to retell the story.

Name _____

As I read, I will pay attention to pauses, stops, and intonation.

	The year is 1631. Shah Jahan is the Muslim emperor of India. He is
13	a member of the royal Mughal (MOO-gul) family. He has three wives,
24	but his favorite is the beautiful, beloved Mumtaz Mahal (MUM-tahz
33	MUH-hahl). She is the one who goes with him when he leads his armies.
46	She is his close friend and companion. She is the love of his life.
60	Shah Jahan is a man who enjoys enormous wealth. He rules from a
73	solid gold throne covered in hundreds of jewels: diamonds, pearls,
83	rubies, and emeralds. His throne is so colorful, it is called the Peacock
96	Throne. Anything he desires, he has. Anything Shah Jahan wants to do,
108	he does.
110	His beloved Mumtaz becomes ill after giving birth to their fourteenth
121	child. She is dying, and Shah Jahan, for all his wealth and power, can do
136	nothing. Mumtaz knows her end is near. She whispers to Shah Jahan,
148	asking for a promise. He agrees to follow her dying wish. There is
161	nothing that he would not do for her. Later, stories are told of his black
176	hair turning white from grief. 181

Comprehension Check

1. Before Shah Jahan's wife died, how do you think his wealth made him feel? **Make Generalizations**

2. How was Shah Jahan's life before his wife died? How do you think his life was different after she died? **Compare and Contrast**

	Words Read	−	Number of Errors	=	Words Correct Score
First Read		−		=	
Second Read		−		=	

At Home: Help the student read the passage, paying attention to the goal at the top of the page.

Leonardo's Horse • Grade 6/Unit 6

189

Name _____

Primary sources are records that were written or created at the time events occurred. They may include diaries, newspapers, manuscripts, or letters. Documents produced by the government may also be considered primary sources. Some primary sources are not written but may be ancient roads, buildings, or tools.

The following is a quote by an American architect. Read the quote. Then answer the questions.

"In the Southwest, Pueblo-style adobe buildings are among the most ecologically friendly structures in the world. The adobe material comes from the earth itself. Adobe is typically a mixture of water, clay, and straw that has been formed into blocks and then baked in the sun. An adobe home blends into the desert around it. The structure is built to withstand the harshness of desert life. The thickness of the walls provides a cool interior during the heat of the desert summer. The thickness also shields from cruel winter temperatures. Even the shape of some Pueblo villages remind you of the cliff walls and canyons of the surrounding desert. Frank Lloyd Wright would have been pleased with the organic quality of these designs."

1. What kind of information does the excerpt give?

_____

_____

2. Why might this primary source be useful?

_____

_____

At Home Talk about writing letters with the student.

Many English words have **Greek roots**. These roots cannot always stand alone as words. Knowing Greek root meanings can help you find the meanings of English words.

The Greek root *phil* means "to like or love". The Greek root *sofia* means "wisdom." A *philosopher* is a lover of wisdom.

Make as many words as possible with the Greek roots below. Use a dictionary if necessary.

1. Greek root *arch,* which means "ancient or chief"

   _____

   _____

2. Greek root *bibli,* which means "book"

   _____

   _____

3. Greek root *cosm,* which means "world or order"

   _____

   _____

4. Greek root *dem,* which means "people"

   _____

   _____

5. Greek root *astr,* which means "stars or planets"

   _____

6. Greek root *polit,* which means "citizen, government, city"

   _____

   _____

© Macmillan/McGraw-Hill

 At Home Have the student make a word with the Greek root *hydr,* which means "water".

Name _____

When you know the meaning of some common **Greek and Latin prefixes**, you can figure out the meaning of many words. Here is a chart of some common prefixes and their meanings. Note that *co*, *com*, and *con* all come from the same root.

Prefix	Meaning of Prefix	Example Word	Word Meaning
co, com, con	together or with	contract	pull together
post	after	postpone	place after
pro	in front of or for	proportion	a portion in relation to a whole
sub	under	submarine	under the sea

If you do not know the meaning of a word and you forget what the prefix means, think of another word that has the same prefix. This can also help you understand new words.

Examples: conduct, constrict   postmark, postseason

Read the following words and underline their Greek or Latin prefixes. Then write the meaning of the word on the line following it. Use a dictionary to help.

1. Prefix *co,* meaning "with, together"

   correspondence _____

2. Prefix *post,* meaning "after, following"

   postscript _____

3. Prefix *pro,* meaning "forward, in place of"

   pronoun _____

4. Prefix *sub,* meaning "under, beneath"

   subway _____

At Home Have the student use the Greek prefix *peri* in a word.

| immigrated | honorable | tinkering | destination |
| fidget | formally | glumly | unsteady |

A. Circle the context clues that help you determine the meaning of the underlined words.

1. Leandros <u>immigrated</u> from the country where he was born to this country.

2. Someone who runs for office should be <u>honorable</u> and moral.

3. Marilyn enjoys <u>tinkering</u> and staying aimlessly busy.

4. The final stop and <u>destination</u> was Los Angeles.

5. "Don't <u>fidget</u>," Marilyn said to her restless, squirming brother.

6. Ballroom dancing requires you to act <u>formally</u> and politely.

7. Maria looked sadly and <u>glumly</u> at the remains of her snowman.

8. The ladder was shaky and <u>unsteady</u>.

B. Write the letter of the definition beside each vocabulary word in the first column.

9. immigrated ____

10. honorable ____

11. tinkering ____

12. destination ____

13. fidget ____

14. formally ____

15. glumly ____

16. unsteady ____

a. make restless movements

b. drearily, gloomily

c. moral

d. not stable or steady

e. place to which you travel

f. busy in an aimless way

g. acting with polite behavior

h. moved to a new country

Name _____

Events in a story happen in a certain order or **sequence**. Understanding the sequence of events can help you better understand what you read.

Read each of the two descriptions below. The events are out of sequence. Number the events in the order in which they should occur.

_____ Jeffrey draws sketches of a time machine.

_____ Jeffrey makes his first trip into the future on a Saturday night.

_____ He builds the time machine in his basement.

_____ Jeffrey is a young scientist who wants to visit the future.

_____ Then he decides to test it out.

_____ While they were camping, it rained.

_____ The family discovered their old tent had holes.

_____ Mei's family decided to go camping.

_____ Mei's family had to buy a new tent.

_____ The family made a list of camping items to pack.

At Home Have the student list in sequence what he or she does in the morning before school.

© Macmillan/McGraw-Hill

Name _____

As you read *LAFFF* fill in the Sequence Chart.

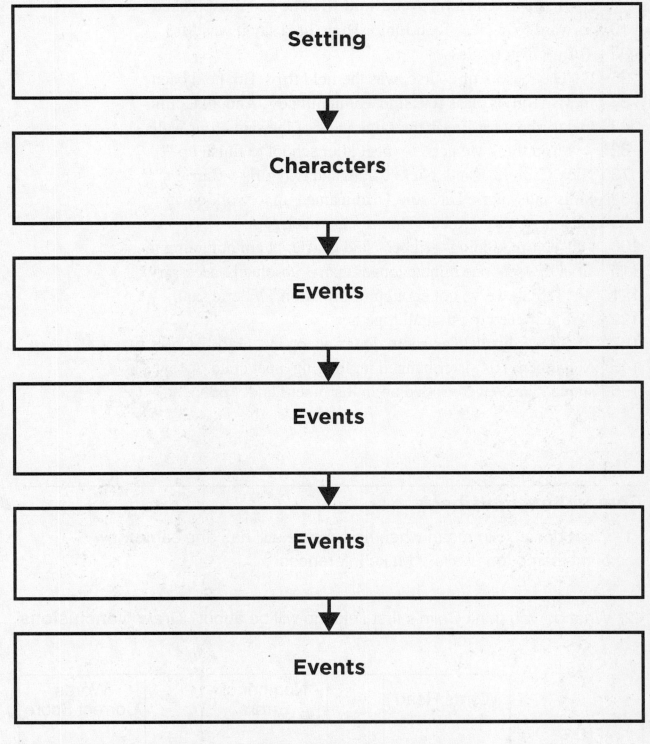

Setting

↓

Characters

↓

Events

↓

Events

↓

Events

↓

Events

How does the information you wrote in this Sequence Chart help you monitor comprehension of *LAFFF*?

At Home: Have the student use the chart to retell the story.

© Macmillan/McGraw-Hill

As I read, I will pay attention to punctuation and characters' voices.

	If you asked Colin Woodward what he had most looked
10	forward to at New Tech Junior High, he'd say it was Ms.
22	Tolly's history class.
25	The reason, of course, was the field trips. But he'd been
36	in Ms. Tolly's class for almost a month now. And all Colin
48	had to show for it was the same view of the same four walls.
62	"You think we need to meet after school to finish up?"
73	Nick Cabrera asked. Nick, Colin, and two girls—Carrie
82	Sims and Valerie Dawson—had teamed up to work on an
93	ancient history project. Their focus was Egypt.
100	"You're kidding—right?" said Carrie. "I am not going to
110	sit in this seat one minute longer than is absolutely necessary."
121	"I think we've got enough information," Valerie said.
129	"We just need to put it all together."
137	Suddenly, the classroom door flew open. "Gilly!" Colin
145	exclaimed. His sister banged in, lugging a pet crate. A few
156	stapled pages were rolled up in her other hand. 165

Comprehension Check

1. What does Colin mean when he says he still has "the same view of the same four walls"? Make Inferences

2. What do you think Colin's first field trip will be about? **Draw Conclusions**

	Words Read	–	Number of Errors	=	Words Correct Score
First Read		–		=	
Second Read		–		=	

© Macmillan/McGraw-Hill

 At Home: Help the student read the passage, paying attention to the goal at the top of the page.

The Internet can be used to find information. When you type in the **keywords** of a topic in which you are interested, the search engine explores the Internet and brings up a list of underlined words called **hyperlinks**. Clicking on a hyperlink will take you to a Web site related to the topic for which you are searching.

Frank Lloyd Wright (June 8, 1867–April 9, 1959) was one of the most well-known <u>architects</u> of the 20th century. He was born in Richland Center, Wisconsin. As a child, Wright played with <u>Kindergarten educational blocks</u>. These geometric blocks could easily form three-dimensional designs. Wright spoke about how the blocks influenced his future career. Many of his buildings, like <u>Larkin Building</u> and <u>Robie Residence,</u> have strong geometrical lines that remind the viewer of children's building blocks.

1. What keywords were used to find this Web site? _____

2. Why do you think the word "architects" is a hyperlink? _____
   _____

3. Why do you think "Kindergarten educational blocks" is a
   hyperlink? _____
   _____

4. If you wanted to see pictures of some of Frank Lloyd Wright's buildings,
   what keywords could you use? _____

5. How could you find out more about the Larkin Building? _____
   _____

At Home: Ask the student to name some famous buildings
that architects have designed.

Name _____

> **Synonyms** are words that have the same or nearly the same meaning. The denotation of a word is the specific definition, the one you would find in a dictionary. Some words have additional meanings, emotions, and associations. These are the connotation of the word. Connotations can be negative or positive. For instance, the denotation of *glumly*—its actual dictionary definition–is "drearily, gloomily." But *glumly* can also include the way a person is sullen and resentful.

Study the following sets of words. Identify which word has a negative connotation. Explain the difference between the two words. Use a dictionary if necessary.

1. thrifty / stingy

_____

_____

2. nosy / curious

_____

_____

3. childish / playful

_____

_____

4. scrawny / slender

_____

_____

5. picky / selective

_____

_____

At Home Have the student choose the word from this pair with a negative connotation: lazy / inactive.

Name _____

Greek suffixes can be added to roots or base words to make new words. Here are some Greek suffixes that you may know.

Suffix	Meaning of Suffix	Example Word	Word Meaning
-logy, *-ology*	the study or the science of (the root)	biology	the study of life
-ician	one who specializes in (the root)	physician	a doctor; one who specializes in the physical
-crat	believer in (the root)	democrat	a believer in the people

If you do not know the meaning of a word and you forget what the suffix means, think of another word that has the same suffix. This can help you understand new words.

Look at each root and add the Greek suffix to it, as indicated. Write the word on the line. Then write the meaning of the word on the second line.

1. geo + -logy _____

_____

2. beaut + -ician _____

_____

3. auto + *-crat* _____

_____

4. mus + *-ician* _____

_____

At Home Have the student write some more words that have Greek suffixes.

Name _____

Each underlined vocabulary word is shown in context in the following sentences.

- I enjoy reading books by <u>anthropologists</u>, people who study the characteristics of civilizations.

- <u>Presumably</u>, anthropologists attend universities to study in their field.

- The stagehands put up the <u>portable</u> lighting and sound system before the show.

- The people who touch paintings in a museum are more than just a <u>nuisance</u>.

- The replica of a Viking ship in the historical museum was <u>immense</u>.

A. Write the definition of each vocabulary word on the line provided.

1. anthropologists _____

_____

2. presumably _____

3. portable _____

4. nuisance _____

5. immense _____

B. Choose three vocabulary words and write sentences for them.

6. _____

7. _____

8. _____

Name _____

Knowing how to identify a **problem** and paying attention to its **solution** will help you better understand and enjoy any articles you read. Look at the following sentences:

Sicilian, a language spoken on the island of Sicily in Italy, is a dying language. University students from the capital city of Palermo are interviewing people who still speak the language, hoping to capture it on CD.

The problem is that the Sicilian language is dying.

The solution, or answer, to the problem, is to capture the language on CD.

Read each problem below about keeping in touch. Then describe the solution for each problem.

1. Problem: Early settlers in the colonies wrote letters to each other, but they did not have a reliable way to send them.

   Solution: _____

   _____

2. Problem: Business people in the United States and Europe could not communicate with each other except by letters on mail boats, which took weeks to deliver.

   Solution: _____

   _____

3. Problem: People in the early 1900s wanted telephones, but the systems were too small to allow many people to have them.

   Solution: _____

   _____

4. Problem: Students and professors at Stanford University wanted to communicate with each other without using the telephone.

   Solution: _____

   _____

At Home: Have the student provide a solution to a problem you pose.

These Walls Can Talk
Grade 6/Unit 6

201

Name _____

As you read *These Walls Can Talk,* fill in the Problem and Solution Chart.

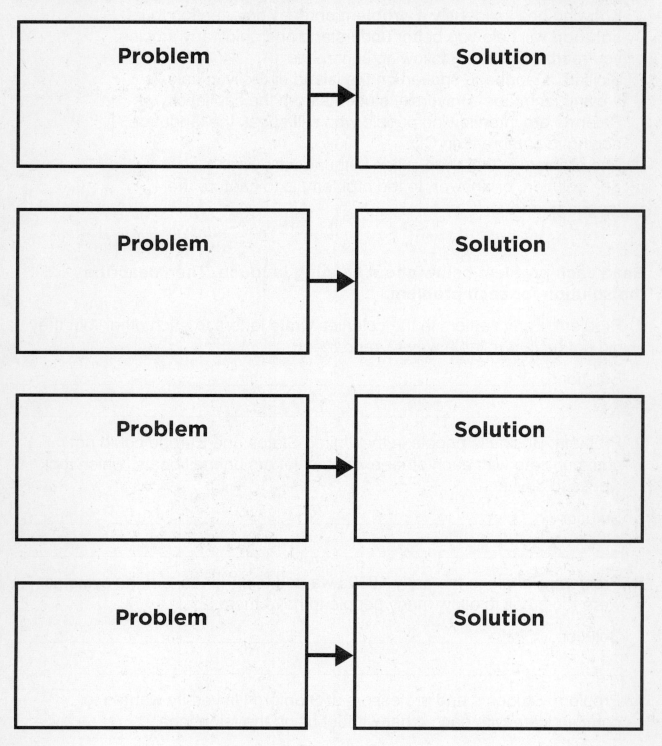

Problem	Solution

Problem	Solution

Problem	Solution

Problem	Solution

How does the information you wrote in this Problem and Solution Chart
help you monitor comprehension of *These Walls Can Talk*?

 At Home: Have the student use the chart to retell the story.

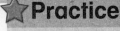

Name _____

As I read, I will pay attention to pronunciation of vocabulary and other difficult words.

	Most scholars think that writing started in many different places
10	around the same time. They believe that writing began by combining
21	pictures with signs. Each picture or sign had a meaning. Viewers could
33	guess the meaning of a sign because it suggested the shape of the object
47	it represented; for instance, the signs that mean water and star are both
60	quite similar in different cultures.
65	**Anthropologists** think that early people valued writing because they
74	created myths about it. Some saw writing as a gift from the gods.
87	Writing with pictures and signs has some problems. First some things
98	are hard to picture. How do you show respect, for instance? Also the
111	number of pictures or signs can become very large.
120	Over time people solved these problems by creating new ways of
131	writing. One method is called mixed script. This uses marks as well as
144	pictures. The marks stand for different sounds. 151

Comprehension Check

1. What problem did picture writing cause? What is one solution? **Problem and Solution**

2. What generalization did scholars make about early writing? **Make Generalizations**

	Words Read	–	Number of Errors	=	Words Correct Score
First Read		–		=	
Second Read		–		=	

 At Home: Help the student read the passage, paying attention to the goal at the top of the page

Name _____

In your life as a reader, you will not simply be reading words. Often, you will have to read and comprehend **functional documents**. These documents are things you need to understand in order to accomplish a task. Examples of functional documents are directions, consumer materials, and advertisements.

Pedro wants to buy a new racing bike. He sees the advertisements below in the window of the bike shop. Use the ads to answer the questions.

Sale			
20-inch MOTOCROSS BIKE $69.99	20-inch HIGH RISER BIKE $49.99	24-inch DELUXE 10-SPEED BIKE $94.99	20-inch BIKE with training wheels $39.99

1. Pedro wants a bike with many speeds. Which one should he look at?

_____

2. Which bike costs $49.99?

_____

3. If Pedro wanted to buy a bike for his four-year-old sister, which bike might he look at?

_____

4. Pedro knows from shopping on the Internet that the true cost of the 24-inch Deluxe 10-speed bike is $65.00. What is the markup, or the amount of money the store adds for its profit? Explain your answer.

_____

_____

 At Home: Ask the student which of the bikes above he or she would buy.

Name _____

Words are often made of parts. These parts, called prefixes, suffixes, base words, and roots, may come from different languages, such as Latin or Greek. Familiarizing yourself with **Latin and Greek word parts** can help you determine the meanings of English words.

A. **Write a word with the Latin or Greek word parts below. Use a dictionary if necessary.**

1. Latin root *bene,* which means "good" with the suffix *-diction*

   _____

2. Greek root *log* or *logi,* which means "speech, reason, science" with the suffix *-ic*

   _____

3. Latin root *tract,* which means "draw or pull" with the suffix *-or*

   _____

4. Greek root *phono,* which means "sound" with the suffix *-graph*

   _____

5. Latin root *capit,* which means "head" with the suffix *-al*

   _____

B. **Choose one of the words you wrote and use it in a sentence of your own.**

6. _____

   _____

   _____

At Home: Have the student make some words from the Greek root *geo,* meaning "earth."

These Walls Can Talk
Grade 6/Unit 6

205

When you find words with **absorbed prefixes**, such as *ac-, ar-, il-, im-,* or *ir-,* you can recognize them because you drop the final consonant of the prefix and you double the first letter of the root or base word. You break the word into syllables between the doubled consonant.
Example: immigrate = im/mi/grate

Say each word aloud. Then write the word with the syllables divided by slashes.

1. illegal _____

2. immobile _____

3. attain _____

4. occupy _____

5. illuminate _____

6. arrest _____

7. commute _____

8. arrive _____

9. announce _____

10. illogical _____

206 These Walls Can Talk
Grade 6/Unit 6

At Home: Have the student divide the word
immature into syllables.

© Macmillan/McGraw-Hill

Name _____

manuscripts	established	scribes	guilds
obstacles	alloy	penniless	privileged

Read the following sentences. Each underlined word is a vocabulary word.

- Becky found a box containing old <u>manuscripts</u> in the bookstore.

- The bookstore had <u>established</u> a reading group earlier that year.

- The group learned about <u>scribes</u>, who wrote manuscripts in the Middle Ages.

- The group also studied the various <u>guilds</u> that formed at that time.

- Becky had to overcome many <u>obstacles</u> to get to the book store.

- Gutenberg used a metal <u>alloy</u> for casting his type.

- Becky wondered how Gutenberg felt when he discovered he was <u>penniless</u>.

- She felt <u>privileged</u> to have been invited to join the reading group.

Write the letter of the definition beside each vocabulary word in the first column.

1. manuscripts ____   **a.** having no money

2. established ____   **b.** enjoying benefit or favor

3. scribes ____   **c.** associations of merchants or craftspeople

4. guilds ____   **d.** a metal formed of two or more metals

5. obstacles ____   **e.** a written or typewritten composition

6. alloy ____   **f.** people who copy manuscripts

7. penniless ____   **g.** introduced or caused to grow

8. privileged ____   **h.** things that hinder progress

When you describe something in words, you want to create a striking visual image for your readers. Use vivid, descriptive details to tell your reader how the subject looks, sounds, smells, tastes, or feels.

Look at the list of events below. Each one appeals to the senses of sight and sound, as well as smell. Choose one, circle it, and answer the questions that follow.

A campfire where campers are roasting marshmallows

A hayride where teenagers are singing

A state fair where cotton candy and popcorn are being made

1. What smells go along with this scene? _____

_____

_____

_____

_____

2. What sounds do you hear? _____

_____

_____

_____

_____

3. What tastes go along with this scene? _____

_____

4. What might appeal to your sense of touch? _____

_____

_____

At Home: Have the student describe something in the room where you are sitting, using all five senses.

Name _____

As you read *Breaking into Print,* fill in the Description Web.

How does the information you wrote in this Description Web help you monitor comprehension of *Breaking into Print*?

 At Home: Have the student use the chart to retell the story.

Breaking into Print • **Grade 6/Unit 6** **209**

Name _____

As I read, I will pay attention to tempo.

	When you were a baby, little by little you learned to talk.
12	At first, you tried to name the people around you. *Mama,*
23	*Dada,* you might have said as they smiled at you. Then you
35	learned to point to objects you wanted, and to make a sound
47	like the name for the object. *Bah, bah,* perhaps you said,
58	as you pointed to the ball in the corner. As your language
70	skills improved, you began to use sentences. *I want a cookie*
81	could be an example of a simple first sentence.
90	As you grew older, you began to get a sense of time. You
103	understood the difference between the past and the present.
112	You could place yourself and your actions in time.
121	In your mind, you began to have a history. And, like all
133	humans, you wanted to share that history. *I played with the*
144	*ball. Then I ate a cookie.* You began to tell stories about
156	yourself and the world around you. Your stories are part of a
168	tradition that has been passed on for centuries. But why do
179	we tell stories? 182

Comprehension Check

1. How would you describe how babies learn to talk? **Description**

2. Why is language so important? **Make Generalizations**

	Words Read	–	Number of Errors	=	Words Correct Score
First Read		–		=	
Second Read		–		=	

© Macmillan/McGraw-Hill

At Home: Help the student read the passage, paying attention to the goal at the top of the page.

Name _____

★ **Practice**
Literary Elements:
Rhyme Scheme,
Rythmic Patterns, and
Personification

> A **rhyme scheme** is the pattern made by the end rhymes in a poem. Schemes are represented by lowercase letters that show the rhymes, such as aabb or ccdd.
>
> Rhyme schemes create a **rhythmic pattern** or predictable ending for each stanza of a poem.
>
> **Personification** is a figure of speech in which human qualities are given to animals, ideas, or objects.

Read the following poem. Then answer the questions.

The Sky Is Low, The Clouds Are Mean
by Emily Dickinson

The Sky is low — the Clouds are mean.
A Traveling Flake of Snow
Across a Barn or through a Rut
Debates if it will go —

A Narrow Wind complains all Day
How someone treated him
Nature, like Us is sometimes caught
Without her Diadem.*
*crown

1. Find examples of rhyme in the poem. _____

2. What is the rhyme scheme? _____

3. Find an example of personification in the poem. _____

   _____

4. What is Dickinson saying in this poem? _____

   _____

   _____

At Home: Read the poem aloud with the student and discuss it.

Name _____

Many English words have **Latin roots**. Familiarizing yourself with Latin root meanings will help you determine the meanings of English words. These roots cannot always stand alone as words. The Latin root *man* or *manu* means "hand."
The Latin root *script* means "write." A *manuscript* is material written by hand or typewritten.

Write as many words as possible from the Latin roots below. Use a dictionary if necessary.

1. Latin root *vis* or *vid,* which means "see" _____

_____

_____

2. Latin root *spir,* which means "breath" _____

_____

3. Latin root *reg, rig, rect,* which means "rule, straight, right" _____

_____

_____

_____

4. Latin root *prim,* which means "first, early" _____

_____

_____

5. Latin root *pend, pens,* which means "hang or weigh" _____

_____

_____

At Home: Have the student use the word *invisible* in a sentence.

Many words in English come from Greek and Roman **mythology**. The gods and goddesses of these early myths had certain characteristics that are shown in the modern words formed from their names. An example of a word taken from mythology is *cereal.* This word is from *Ceres,* the Roman goddess of agriculture, because *cereal* is made from grain.

Study the words below that are based on Greek or Roman mythology. Use each word in a sentence of your own.

1. east: from Eos, the Greek goddess of the dawn _____

_____

2. flower: from Flora, the Roman goddess of flowers _____

_____

3. March, martial: from Mars, the Roman god of war _____

_____

4. volcano: from Vulcan, the Roman god of fire _____

_____

5. Saturday, Saturn: from Saturn, the Roman god of agriculture _____

_____

6. January: from Janus, the Roman god of beginnings _____

_____

7. May: from Maia, the Roman goddess of growth _____

_____

8. hypnosis: from Hypnos, the Greek god of sleep _____

_____

At Home: Have the student use the word
jovial in a sentence.

Breaking into Print • **Grade 6/Unit 6**

213

Name _____

A. Each underlined vocabulary word is shown in context in the following sentences. Circle the content clue in each sentence.

1. Joshua's house, or <u>dwelling</u>, was in the path of the volcano.

2. Joshua was an <u>ambitious</u> boy; he wanted to achieve something.

3. Joshua did not waste time and <u>lounge</u> about in lazy way.

4. He spent his days <u>pondering</u>, thinking about what to do next.

5. When he felt <u>drowsy</u> and sleepy, he took a nap.

6. The nap usually <u>revived</u> him, and he felt his energy restored

7. Joshua <u>agonized</u>, really suffered, about the decision to move away from the volcano.

8. He knew if the volcano erupted, he would not be able to breathe the gases and <u>vapors</u>.

B. Write the definition of each vocabulary word on the line provided.

9. dwelling _____

10. ambitious _____

11. lounge _____

12. pondering _____

13. drowsy _____

14. revived _____

15. agonized _____

16. vapors _____

Name _____

> The **theme** is the main idea or message of a story. Authors often do not state the theme directly. It is revealed through the interaction of the characters, actions, and conflict.

Read each passage and circle the theme that best states the main idea or message.

1. April received a package from an on-line bookstore. She opened it and found the latest book from her favorite mystery series. She looked in the box to discover who had sent the package. A slip fell out which said, "We all know how much you like Miss Story's Mysteries. So we knew exactly how to reward your work. Happy reading!" There was no signature. She smiled because now she knew who had sent the book.

   You should work hard to be rewarded.

   Your efforts may be rewarded unexpectedly.

   You should tell people what you like to read.

2. Malcolm did not want to rappel down a cliff wall. His remembered his instructor's speech after they had put on their climbing harnesses and other equipment. His instructor had said that it was normal to be scared, but it was important for them to trust the safety equipment and follow directions. Malcolm was scared, but he also knew that he would be very proud once he completed this rappel. He took a deep breath and told the instructor he was ready.

   It is important to listen and follow safety directions.

   Always take a risk because you don't know what will happen.

   Don't let fear keep you from accomplishing goals.

 At Home: Together, discuss with the student what the passages would say if they had one of the other themes.

The Dog of Pompeii • Grade 6/Unit 6   215

As you read *The Dog of Pompeii,* fill in the Theme Chart.

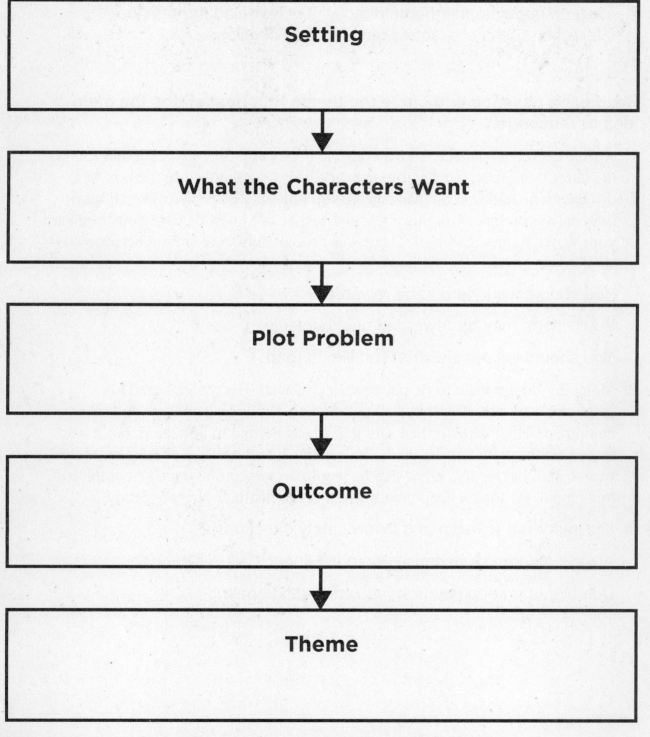

Setting

↓

What the Characters Want

↓

Plot Problem

↓

Outcome

↓

Theme

How does the information you wrote in this Theme Chart help you
monitor comprehension of *The Dog of Pompeii*?

© Macmillan/McGraw-Hill

At Home: Have the student use the chart to retell the story.

Name _____

As I read, I will pay attention to pauses and intonation.

	In November 1984, a volcano began rumbling high in the Andes
10	Mountains in Colombia. The volcano was Nevado del Ruiz (nay-VAHD-oh
19	DEL-roo-EES). During the next year, it showed more signs of restlessness.
29	**Vapors** escaped from the top of the volcano, and minor earthquakes occurred.
41	Nevado del Ruiz often belched clouds of steam and other gases.
52	This increased activity was a sign that something more dramatic was going
64	to happen. But when would it happen?
71	Twice, in 1595 and in 1845, eruptions from Nevado del Ruiz caused
81	mudflows that killed hundreds of people.
87	On the afternoon of November 13, 1985, Nevado del Ruiz erupted
96	violently. Ash and gases spewed into the sky. Two hours later, the ash and
110	pieces of rock rained down on the town of Armero [ahr-MER-oh].The town
122	was located miles away from the volcano.
129	Community leaders assured citizens that there was nothing to fear. People
140	in the town remained calm. After all, the officials hadn't asked them to leave
154	town. When the ash stopped falling around 7:00 in the evening, everyone felt
166	greatly relieved. 168

Comprehension Check

1. How do you know what the word *spewed* means? **Make Inferences**

2. What events happened in the year before the volcano erupted? **Sequence**

	Words Read	–	Number of Errors	=	Words Correct Score
First Read		–		=	
Second Read		–		=	

At Home: Help the student read the passage, paying attention to the goal at the top of the page

The Dog of Pompeii • **Grade 6/Unit 6**

217

© Macmillan/McGraw-Hill

Articles in magazines, newspapers, and textbooks are often accompanied by photos or other **graphic aids**. Photos enrich an article by showing the reader something words cannot. Often a photo or drawing is accompanied by a caption, a sentence or two beneath the illustration. Captions describe what is in the picture, and often give the reader additional information.

Study the drawing and caption below. Use them to answer the questions.

Mount Etna is a volcano located on the island of Sicily, off the coast of Italy. Its name comes from the ancient Greek word *aitho*, which means "I burn." Mount Etna is 3,350 meters above sea level. It is Europe's highest active volcano.

1. What is shown in the drawing? _____

2. Where is it located? _____

    _____

3. How did it get its name? _____

    _____

4. What is its height? _____

5. What other information does the caption give? _____

    _____

 At Home: Together, look through newspapers, magazines, or books for other examples of graphic aids.

Name _____

Many words have more than one definition. These are called **multiple-meaning words**. Often, you can use context clues, or the information that surrounds a multiple-meaning word, to help determine its meaning.

Each underlined word below is a multiple-meaning word. Use the context clues to determine its meaning in the sentence. Then, on the blank, write the letter of the correct meaning.

1. Daniel likes to <u>lounge</u> around, resting on the couch and watching TV. ____
   Mom wants to buy a <u>lounge</u> for this corner of the family room. ____
   The club has a private <u>lounge</u> where members can talk and relax together. ____

   a. a room for leisure activities   **b.** act or move lazily
   c. a long couch

2. Daniel drew <u>fine</u> lines on the paper. ____
   Dad had to pay a <u>fine</u> for his overdue library books. ____
   Dad said, "That's a <u>fine</u> drawing, Daniel." ____

   a. money paid as a penalty   **b.** very good; excellent
   c. very thin or delicate

3. The <u>object</u> of the game of chess is to capture the king. ____
   Daniel will <u>object</u> when I tell him he has to do the dishes tonight. ____
   Dad gave Daniel a mysterious <u>object</u> for his birthday. ____

   a. a goal or purpose   **b.** to protest or argue
   c. a thing

4. Daniel will <u>stand</u> when his grandmother comes into the room. ____
   Dad said, "I need to know where you <u>stand</u> on this, Daniel." ____
   The judge said, "Will you please take the <u>stand</u> now?" ____

   a. a place taken by a   **b.** to have an opinion about
   witness for testifying in court   something
   c. to be upright on one's feet

At Home: Have the student use one of the words above in a sentence.

The Dog of Pompeii • **Grade 6/Unit 6**

219

Name _____

Many words in English come from other languages. The word *sombrero,* for example, is a Spanish word. A sombrero is a hat with a wide brim. The word *sombra* in Spanish means "shade," so a sombrero is a hat that shades you from the sun.

Study the words below taken from around the world. Use each word in a sentence of your own. Use a dictionary if necessary.

1. bazaar: from Persian; a market consisting of rows of shops _____

_____

2. bronco: from Spanish; an unbroken range horse, like a Mustang

_____

3. caribou: from an Indian language, Micmac; a large deer _____

_____

4. denim: from French "serge de Nimes;" a firm, cotton fabric _____

_____

5. gong: from Malayan; a disk-shaped percussion instrument _____

_____

6. igloo: from Inuit; an Eskimo house shaped like a dome _____

_____

7. algebra: from Arabic; a mathematical science _____

_____

8. typhoon: from Mandarin; a "big wind" _____

_____

At Home: Have the student use the word *denim* in a sentence.

Name _____

A. Choose a vocabulary word from the box to answer each question. Write your answer on the line provided.

| philosopher | recommend | honorable | fidget | unsteady |

1. What is another word for not stable? _____

2. What is another way to say speak of favorably? _____

3. What is a word for a person who seeks wisdom? _____

4. What is a word that means having a good reputation? _____

5. What does someone do who is restless? _____

B. Use the correct vocabulary words from the box to make sense in the sentences below.

| miniature | formally | portable | nuisance | alloy |

6. The doll house had furniture in _____.

7. There is a _____ stage in that big truck.

8. Gutenberg made his type from an _____ of different metals.

9. The new puppy was adorable but was also a pesky _____.

10. The president will be _____ inducted at the banquet.

Name _____

A. Choose a vocabulary word from the box to answer each question. Write your answer on the line provided.

| glumly | envisioned | immense | obstacles | penniless |

1. What is another word for great in size? _____

2. What is another way to say drearily, gloomily? _____

3. What do you call things that impede progress? _____

4. What is a word that means to picture to oneself? _____

5. What word means you have no money? _____

B. Use the vocabulary words from the box below in sentences of your own.

| ambitious | pondering | drowsy | agonized | guilds |

6. _____

7. _____

8. _____

9. _____

10. _____